STEERING CURRENTS

STEERING CURRENTS

by Vicki Armitage

STEERING CURRENTS

PUBLISHED BY
Serendipity Press
Fairhope, Alabama
Http://www.serendipitypress.org

Names, characters, and places in some instances have been changed.

Subjects: Dance, Coastal, Southern, Fairhope, Spirituality, Business, Women

ISBN 978-1-7323174-7-5

Printed in the United States of America

Type face: Times New Roman

Cover design by Phyllis Pittman

Cover Photo by Vories

ACKNOWLEDGEMENTS

I thank God for allowing me to be subjected to the intensity of life's storms and for the courage to finally speak about that. Like many, I was in a comfort zone of sorts, believing I was on a path that was best for me and those I loved. I'm thankful for those women at the dance studio who helped to keep my eyes lifted toward each new day.

I am grateful for this little community in Alabama, its residents, my cherished friends, neighbors, and strangers who welcomed me at every turn. The gentle environment, the natural beauty, and rich creativity were healing for my soul.

And there were those who nurtured me as a writer: the Aspen Writer's Foundation and Aspen Words brought together the best in the literary world, most recently Dani Shapiro, who gathered a few of us in her living room for several days, such encouragement. And Joan Anderson, my dear friend and brilliant New York Times bestselling author, her support and encouragement, such a gift. Anne, confidante and mentor, thank you. The Fairhope Writer's Group, what an intimate and fertile setting, each of you providing feedback on many chapters in this book. Rosemerry and Augusta, your Soul Writer's Group continues to be a rich and safe environment for learning the process and ourselves. Serendipity Press and Phyllis Pittman, much gratitude for your attention to detail, creativity, and unmatched savvy. Vories for your amazing photography, cherished friendship, and encouragement.

My family: children Kelly and Robby; grandchildren Ashlee, Madeline, Jillian, and Jack. More than anyone, you each spoke the words, "Do You!" It's a current catchphrase that reminded me that we each have been assigned our life to live—it also reminds me to stay curious and cultivate wonder, take the next right step, and allow my heart to be filled with love that spills out on anyone who crosses my path. May we all live with ease.

A NOTE FROM VICKI

A popular song in the 60s was *Turn, Turn, Turn* by The Byrds. "To everything (Turn,Turn, Turn) there is a season (Turn, Turn, Turn) and a time for every purpose under heaven." It was based on the passage from Ecclesiastes. This is the story of a season I did not choose-and, like all seasons, I had no assurance of things getting better. Those who infused my days with shreds of faith and hope kept me buoyed. For that, I am forever grateful. This book is my story from my perspective. A few names have been modified but most are unchanged.

Meteorologists describe the unseen atmospheric currents, streams of air and ribbons of water temperature as steering currents. These currents are used to forecast impending weather disturbances. Advanced diagnostics can predict the course of most storms by closely examining the subtle indicators.

In life, these currents are the quiet nudges that inform or warn us, directing our path and protecting us from the unseen. And, sometimes, we will end up in a place we never expected to be. I pray that for each of you, these currents will lead to calm seas and a life of ease, confident that you find shelter from the storms.

Vicki

STEERING CURRENTS

CHAPTER ONE

It was something more than curiosity that led me into the swamp that morning.

I was on my way to the funeral of someone I'd only met in my dreams. Perhaps I should have let someone know where I was going, but, truly, who would have understood? This little side trip doesn't even qualify as a little eccentric. They'd likely think I'd finally snapped or whatever it is that happens to ordinarily sensible people when their behavior takes a dramatic turn from the norm. Sensible. Not exactly an enviable legacy anyway, I thought as I glanced into the neighborhood below.

I justified this adventure by noting that any women who live south of I-20 have unique qualities that definitely do not include practical, bland, or traditional. A prime example: my red-headed mother, now in her nineties, who wears pantyhose with her swimsuit at the beach. Occasionally, clumps of seaweed will stick to the nylon encasing her feet, creating elaborate trains, collecting seashells and cigarette butts before becoming dislodged. Pantyhose are her perfect accessory for swimming pools, too. Except when chlorine does a number on the elasticity of the spandex. The woman who changed her name to GiGi when grandmotherhood threatened has taught me much. This day felt like an advanced course.

From the interstate, New Orleans' Lower Ninth Ward appeared to be a forgotten wasteland. Bright green weeds emerged through the still life of abandoned cars and houses. I would have expected some activity on a Saturday morning, but dead quiet instead. I realized it may have been smart to check my tires before heading out. That's what sensible people do, for sure. My cell phone did a beep beep that could mean one of two things: low battery or no signal. I looked at the screen: no signal. There went any second thoughts about informing anyone of my whereabouts. Add risk-taker to that legacy. That would be about the last quality anyone used to describe me, prior to now. And that sounded better than lacking sound judgment, anyway. Or unsafe. But, right about now, a little shred of safe sure did sound appealing.

I reached into the cup holder for my half-eaten apple. Bits of previous road trips had attached themselves like on those fancy nut and chocolate numbers. Only this was way more original than any Neiman Marcus high-dollar apple. Focusing on the road, out of the corner of my eye I could see an Altoid, a paper clip, part of a petrified french fry, and something that appeared to be granola but was likely car lint. Fortunately, the other side was intact, although dusty. Realizing I may be holding the only nutrition available until who knew when, I positioned it carefully on a Sonic restaurant napkin on the passenger seat. Up ahead, I saw the exit sign for Destrehan, Louisiana. New Sarpy, my destination, wasn't on the map, so I searched the internet for directions prior to heading out. Since the internet maps were fairly detailed, I wondered if I'd find this place. Sense of direction was not my strong suit, so I glanced again at my cell phone, hoping I could have a back-up plan. *No Signal* blinked repeatedly on the screen, as if to remind me of the obvious: I had entered the unknown. Definitely a place I'd never chosen before now. I was usually the voice of reason. And, right about now, that voice was saying, "You know, Vicki, you could actually get lost very soon."

I had thought the view from the Interstate looked desolate. At ground level, I realized my perception was understated. The two-lane road appeared to be surfaced with a combination of white crushed shell and asphalt; the crunching sound gave me no reassurance about my failure to check the tires. Thankfully, I had filled up before setting out. The only signs of civilization were abandoned gas stations every couple of miles. Nothing else. Then, hope. A green metal sign proclaiming Destrehan. I was close.

I slowed, expecting to see another sign announcing New Sarpy, the place excluded by Google and Rand McNally. Then, in the distance, another green, small sign. I couldn't quite make out the name, but it was one word. I squinted, straining to confirm, contrary to all previous reports, my amazing sense of direction. The sign spelled Norco. *Norco??* According to the internet, New Sarpy was between Destrehan and Norco. So, I attempted to make a U-turn. My SUV wasn't exactly designed for a one-eighty in one smooth move. Careful to stay on the road, since there were no shoulders, it was turn a little, reverse a little, turn a little, until I was once again heading in the opposite direction. That sky-blue convertible I talked myself out of last year would have handled this maneuver perfectly. But I reminded myself that it wasn't as practical or as safe as this brown tank, made for

11

hauling who knows what. Intent on finding the sign that read New Sarpy, I thought I spotted it. There, a green sign! Another squint . . . *Destrehan*?

I reached for my bottle of water, careful to ration what may be essential for hydration very soon. I cranked up the air conditioner and started over. Another U turn and another. There was *no* sign that said New Sarpy. I scanned the road for a turn that looked like it led anywhere. There was only one. It seemed to go straight into the swamp.

Maybe this was the moment I should have said "not meant to be" and gone to Lafayette for gumbo. Maybe this was the confirmation that my nature to plan, organize and, yes, even control a little bit, wasn't all that bad. No sane person sets out for the funeral of a complete stranger miles away from anyone or anything familiar. Maybe Robert Frost *wasn't* implying that taking the road less travelled was a good thing.

As I turned toward the swamp, the steering wheel slipped in my hands—my palms were almost dripping, my heart was pounding, and a serious case of queasy seemed unavoidable. I had allowed plenty of time to be there early, assuming I'd find my way easily. I hadn't counted on this. The black water rose up to the road on both sides. Chartreuse scum formed islands beneath giant decaying cypress trees, their branches so covered with thick, gray tangles of moss the sunlight disappeared. I thought of alligators, water moccasins, flat tires, and crying. If I was on the way to New Sarpy, should I have gotten the message sooner? If you need a sign, then you likely aren't welcome there.

The tiny community seemed to be primarily row houses, most with cobalt-colored tarps covering roofs likely damaged from many storms. A lazy cur dog sprawled halfway in the road, echoing the gaze of the residents who stopped their conversations to study me as I passed. Worn upholstered sofas and chairs provided the vantage from each porch. Barefoot children played chase in dusty, sodless yards, while a toddler girl attempted to put a scrawny, yellow cat in a cardboard box.

New Sarpy Full Gospel Church was beside the railroad track, in the shadow of the mammoth Norco oil refinery. The road dead-ended at the track, a rusted, corrugated metal building on the left and the blond brick church to the right. A narrow drive led to what appeared to be a grassy area behind for parking. As I turned to park, I saw the shiny black hearse arrive and park at the front.

The area in back had been freshly mown and even through the car vents the fragrance of wild, sweet, spring onions and grass cuttings still wet with dew brought me back to childhood and weekends in the country at Grandma's. Making whistles from blades of new grass between my thumbs. Feeling safe and content.

I was still fifty minutes early and the only vehicle in the lot. Making a semi-circle, I backed in close to a row of low scrub bushes. Shoving the gear shift into park, I took a deep breath. Maybe this wasn't a good idea, showing up—a complete stranger—at a time so personal for loved ones and friends. I reached to adjust the air conditioner vent. My hand was trembling. "But she was special to me, too," I heard myself say unconvincingly.

STEERING CURRENTS

At a little after ten-thirty a.m., a line of cars began to stream into the grassy space, parking on either side of me, then making rows in front. As engines were shut off and doors opened, I studied the occupants. Most of the women wore hats, some with netting or feathers or with jeweled brooches attached. Many were dressed as though for a wedding with bright brocades, velvets, lamé, and even gloves. I looked down at my conservative black jacket and pants, a good choice I had thought, sure to blend in.

Within minutes, the entire lot was crowded with cars, even more lining up to park alongside the tracks. Decision time. If I was going in, it had to be very soon. I took a swallow of my now warm water, glanced at myself in the rear-view mirror, and turned off the engine. As I stepped into the grass, a briar snagged my pants. I wondered if this was another sign, discouraging me from going further.

Several men stood outside, each wearing a white carnation. Pallbearers, I assumed. The announcement board beside the front door read, "Homegoing, Mary Washington." A line had formed in the narrow vestibule and I was in it, people following suit behind me. A young woman in a white shirtwaist dress and pearls, maybe in her early twenties, was handing out papers. I reached for one and, without glancing at it, moved forward as the line progressed into the church. All around me, people were embracing, crying, laughing, sharing stories, and reconnecting. I felt both invisible and conspicuous as the processional entered the aisle down the center of the sanctuary. Leaning to my right, I could see that we were in single file to pay our respects. The open casket was a few rows ahead. Then there she was directly in front

14

of me, lying there peacefully—coffee-colored skin, a crimson long-stemmed rose in her hand. I felt warm tears on my cheeks as I whispered, "Thank you, Mary."

Already, the church was filled. I spotted an empty place in the center of a pew, about halfway back. As I edged my way to my seat, I noticed the crowd still coming in. Through the open back doors, I could see the street was full, too. I sat down and reached in my purse for a tissue. Completely drained, I mentally replayed the past week for the hundredth time

*****

I had driven to Birmingham with my daughter, Kelly. We had fun plans to celebrate her birthday with dinner and the Celine Dion concert, then a little shopping the next day before heading back to Enterprise, Alabama. I'd drop her off and leave for home.

I remembered pushing back the curtains in the hotel room and watching the line of rush-hour traffic eight stories below. Blue-gray storm clouds erased the late afternoon light. Strong gusts threatened to pry briefcases from pedestrians scurrying to the parking garage. "I'm thinking I'll wear what I have on," I said.

"Not me," Kelly shouted from the dressing area. "I bought those shoes especially for this trip and I'm gonna look HOT!" Her purchase had been placed tenderly on the white duvet bed covering. Definitely sexy, I thought. Deep pink, patent leather, and open-toed, a black grosgrain ribbon bow on top with matching ribbon that ran back to the graceful, tapered spiked heel.

"On second thought, I may change shoes," I announced as I kicked off my comfy Trekkers. She had turned the shower on, and I pulled a roomy wingback chair to the long window. I tucked my bare feet in beside me and watched the twinkling lights on the river birch trees below flail wildly in the steady wind.

It had felt good to be away. Since she married, Kelly and I didn't have much one-on-one time, other than the telephone. Her suggestion of this girl trip had sounded perfect.

While she was drying her hair, I propped up on the bed, pushing aside the thick covers and heavy, long, bolster pillow. I picked up my phone to check for messages. No calls, but three new e-mails: a sale at Pottery Barn, the pollen report for central Louisiana, and one entitled "Urgent Prayer Request." I opened the prayer request. It was generated by an inspirational daily e-mail I'd been receiving for a few weeks. It began, "Urgent prayer request for our dear Sister, Mary Washington, who suffered a massive heart attack this morning." More details included the name of the hospital and the assurance that updates would follow.

I leaned back against the pillows, suddenly feeling weak and clammy. Kelly had shut off the hair dryer and was standing in front of me, curling iron clamped solidly on a lock of hair below her shoulder. "Mom? You ok?" I glanced at the clock, reached for my bottle of water and patted the bed beside me.

16

"Sit down for a minute; I need to tell you a story." Curling iron still in hand, she complied. "This may sound crazy, Kel, but I've been dreaming about a woman named Mary Washington for years. She appears at times when I'm in some sort of crisis or afraid. Her voice is always soothing and consoling. Sometimes, she'll wrap her arms around me, reminding me that everything is gonna be just fine. Other times, she'll say, 'Now you listen to Mary, baby, this is all gonna work out—just you wait and see.' And then I'll sleep peacefully. This woman, this stranger, has become a comforter for me, showing up from time to time in my dreams when things get rough."

Kelly had this *who are you and what have you done with my mother?* look on her face. "Ok, you're thinking I might want to consider a little therapy, right?"

"Mom, why are you telling me this now?"

"Good question. I've been getting this e-mail devotional for several weeks. One of my dance student's parents put me on the list. It's generated by some organization around New Orleans, a group of women, I think. Tonight, I was checking my e-mail and there's an urgent request from this group requesting prayer for *Mary Washington*. I know, it's crazy, right? You'd think, after all this time, someone by that name would have crossed my path, but this is the first time the name has come up."

"So, Mom, you think we should *pray* or something?"

I shrugged. "Maybe."

Kelly reached out, took my hand, and said, "You go ahead, then."

17

Since this was something we didn't do routinely, I fumbled for words but awkwardly began, "God, Mary Washington is your child and you know her needs. Please give her comfort and peace. And, God, please show me what you want me to know about her." And, together, we whispered, "Amen."

"Now, let's go see Celine!" I said.

The encore song, *My Heart Will Go On*, began "Every night in my dreams, I see you . . ." I pulled my jacket tighter, shivering from something that had nothing to do with the temperature in the arena.

The next morning, I checked e-mail before leaving the hotel. One new message entitled *Mary Washington*. It read, "I am sad to report that our Sister, Mary, left her earthly home . . . Arrangements will be announced as soon as details are available."

Two days later, I left Kelly's, headed toward Louisiana, with a secret plan to attend the funeral of Mary Washington.

*****

Mourners continued to stream into the church as people on both sides scooted in to make room for just one more. I was in full contact, from shoulder to knee, with my seatmates. I exhaled a little, looking around for the first time. A photo of an eagle was on the wall nearest me, beneath it a verse from Isaiah. The organist was arranging her music up on the left of the tiny pulpit. A space for a small choir was empty. Behind the elevated platform was a picture of a dark-skinned Jesus holding a lamb. Laughter and conversation echoed from the shiny floor to the exposed rafters. The clatter of folding chairs being set up behind me indicated the gathering continued to grow.

Pew backs held worn, burgundy Bibles, hymnals, and cardboard hand fans, wooden sticks glued to a photograph of Dr. Martin Luther King. On my immediate left, a large man loosened his tie while reaching for a fan. Removing my jacket sounded very appealing, but I feared I may not fit back in my spot if I stood, even for a moment. I held my purse out in front of me and dropped it on the floor, shoving it under the pew with my foot. I glanced at the program, five ivory pages stapled, a photo of Mary Washington on the cover. A soft voice on my right startled me, "We sho gonna miss our sister, aren't we?" Realizing she was speaking to me, I turned. She appeared to be about my age, slender, in a print dress with abstract splashes of purple, turquoise, black, and red. I nodded, wondering if *I* was going to miss Mary, curious to know if she would continue to appear to me now that dream and reality had merged. "Mmmmmm," was about as much as I could utter, as I nodded solemnly. "My name Dee," she said, extending her hand. Her skin was warm and a bit rough, contrasting my now clammy palm.

"Vicki." I smiled politely. Feeling both grateful and afraid she would ask how I knew Mary, I spoke next, "Do you think she knew how many people loved her?"

"Oh, child, I don't think she ever stopped to think." She laughed. "She was always just following the clues."

"Clues?"

19

"You know, to our treasure," she exclaimed. My head was nodding understanding, but my face must have been absolute puzzlement. She continued, "Yes, indeedy, we all time getting 'em, just most folk ain't hearing. Or ain't listenin'. They sho could keep away from a heap of trouble if they wasn't just doing they own thing."

I swallowed hard and tried to digest this code language, wondering if I'd walked into some sort of cult group that spoke their secrets through this confusing dialog.

Dee continued as she admired the gathering, "Lawd, Mary was some good at reminding us about the clues, said that'd be part of our map. And everybody's map be different, too. She was always sayin', 'Watch for 'em.' We sho can shortchange our callin' and end up where we didn't decide on our own, uhhhhhh huhhhhh."

"I didn't think I'd be here today," I heard myself exclaim.

"I know *that's* right . . ." She was interrupted by an explosion of sound that caused me to jump. I realized I was still holding Dee's hand. She gave me a warm squeeze before jumping to her feet. I wanted to say, "Wait! You know *what's* right, Dee?"

The organist was swaying back and forth, playing something between gospel and rock and roll, accompanied by a drummer somewhere behind her. People were streaming in from every direction, all clapping and singing, "Hallelujah, You Are Worthy!" with an intensity and volume that caused the air to vibrate. Singers wearing black filed in on both sides of the pulpit, doing a side-step along with their clapping, all ages, all in time, filling the choir space and spilling over on the sides. I felt wrapped up in music and sound . . .and something that almost felt like love. More people now, doing the same step, singing the same lyrics, coming from the back and down the sides and the center aisles. All singing, all dancing, all clapping, and a few waving their hands. I was standing and involuntarily swaying with the people in the row, clapping in time. I opened my mouth to sing and, without warning, began sobbing instead. At that moment, Dee turned to me, beaming, bent closer, and said, "Lawd, child, you getting' a clue?"

The heaving sobs became stronger under her scrutiny as she confirmed, "Mary's sho gotta be havin' a party looking down at all a us. Sister, you's havin' a big one, ain't you?"

The floor began to shudder as the family made their way single file into the front pews, some shouting "Glory!" as their side-stepping incorporated shoulders, elbows, upper bodies, too. Both the organist and the drummer were bobbing up and down, side to side, as though they could make the music stronger by their movements. I was gently bounced back and forth between Dee and the big man, whose elbow was level with my neck. Stuffing my wet, pasty ball of tissue into my pocket, I noted it looked like the paper maché cat I tried to create in fourth grade. My hands were free to clap, just about the time double-clapping seemed to take over. Taking a deep breath, I relaxed my shoulders on the exhale. Dee nodded and said, "I know *that's* right!" Again. That was about the time I stopped needing to know what was right.

And then it stopped. A man approached the pulpit, placing one hand on the small wooden podium and gesturing us to sit with the other. "Glory! Pastor Henry gone be preachin' Mary's homegoing," Dee announced to no one in particular. Not thinking about the space limitation, I sat slightly after my seatmates, ending up partly on the lap of each. Not wanting to stand again and start over, I wriggled until I could feel myself on the seat. That began a wriggling and scooching of the entire row until we were all pretty much in our original spots.

Nodding to the familiar members of the congregation, the pastor removed his gold, wire-rimmed glasses, placing them in the chest pocket of his black suitcoat. His slight frame belied his booming articulation. "Our Sister, Mary, has reached out and touched each of us." He stepped down from the platform and began walking down the center aisle. "She touched you." He would point at people and look them dead in the eye with each "and you."

Each one would say, "AMEN!" and raise their hand.

He picked up his pace and was shouting, "You! And you! And you!" Whipping around from one side to the other, like he wanted to surprise people. The organist was punctuating each "you" with a chord, making me wonder if this was the beginning of a tune and we were all about to start singing. "Amens" were being shouted all over. Suddenly, he was at my row, facing the other side, then, there it came, directly at me, "YOU!"

Terrified at what may be next and grateful for Dee shouting, "AMEN!" on my behalf, I held my breath, looked him right back in the eye and nodded agreement, hoping that was enough to keep him moving on. The next thing I knew, he was running back up the aisle to the pulpit, amid a frenzy of "Amens" and hands raised.

Pastor Henry loosened his tie, pulled a white hanky from his pocket, and wiped his face. I leaned an inch toward the big man, hoping to catch a breeze from his Martin Luther King fan.

"I'll never forget the first time Mary came to see me," he continued. "She told me the story of being with a few of you, sitting in her little kitchen, right around the corner from here. Y'all were having a good time, making dirty rice for the Fourth of July fellowship—chopping onions, celery, bell peppers, grinding up the gizzards—laughing and talking about much of nothing. You told me later that all of a sudden, Mary stopped laughing and just stood silent still. Like maybe a chill come over her. But her little window unit wasn't even keeping up, working against the summer swelter and the rice a cooking. One of you asked her what was wrong, did she feel a faint coming on. She wiped her hands on her apron and sat down. If you were in that kitchen on that July afternoon, you remember how all the chopping and talkin' stopped. And she proceeded to tell you about how y'all was supposed to help folks all over the world.

"You see, Mary came to see me because she thought maybe a spirit had come and taken up occupancy in her soul. If you knew her then, you remember how *nothing* scared Mary. Not a hurricane, not a mean ole pit bull, not even that sorry ex-brother-in-law of hers. Sorry 'bout that, Rosa. But this day, she had worry wrote all over her.

"She went on to tell me 'bout how she was in her kitchen with you ladies." He gestured toward his left, about mid-way back. "She told me how y'all was a-laughing and cuttin' up. She claimed she turned to put the lid on the rice and this idea hit her like somebody threw a brick through her window. She started shaking when she said it had to do with reminding people of they clues, especially women folk and they girls."

He started to chuckle, "Lawd, Mary said she didn't even know what that meant! And that it had to be some sort of demon that had got inside a her. She said she'd even start comin' to church regular if I helped make it go away."

I looked at Dee, who was smiling and nodding like she was right there in that kitchen that day. All over the room, people were nodding. I reached for a Martin Luther King fan.

"I told Mary that it had likely gotten too warm in that kitchen, all a y'all in there and cookin' too. But I told her that she could still come to church regular, just in case. For about a month, I didn't see her. Then, one Wednesday night after choir practice, I was locking up and there she was waitin' for me. Said, 'Pastor, I think I got something bad wrong. I keep gettin' these ideas when I'm just goin' about my business. Please, Pastor, I'll do anything, just make them stop.'

"Uhhhhhhh, huhhhhh, I told her. Mary Washington, I think you are getting the clues of the spirit."

'CLUES?' she asked me. 'Pastor, don't you be makin' fun a me right now!'

"'Awww, Mary," I said to her, "I'm thinking you are hearin' your spirit, giving you a vision, an assignment."

24

"'Pastor,' she said, 'I'm a thinkin' I got a spirit, alright. It's jumped inside a me and I don't want to have it be giving me no assignment, ya hear? Now give me a prayer, please, to send it a packin!'

"That was a long night, folks; by the time I got home, my Louise had some foil over my greens and cornbread on the stovetop and had gone to bed. Before Mary left that evening, she had begun to figure out that we's all got a spirit inside a us. And we's all time getting directions, just for us, bout what we need to do. I call 'em clues, like for finding a treasure." He looked at the congregation and said, "So, don't miss it, brothers and sisters, don't miss it!" The big man beside me shouted an amen.

Dee shouted, "I know *that's* right!"

"Mary was all calm when she set out to walk home that night, kinda trying to understand something that couldn't be understood. But after that night, Mary Washington was real different," the pastor concluded.

I sat there, fanning myself, as person after person approached the front and told their story of Mary and how she had helped each of them set out on a new course by reminding them of the clues. Each story was unique, each having moved from a safe predictable life to leaps of faith, taking risks, and making radical changes. A representative from the Ford Foundation had flown in to say how they helped support Mary's vision of connecting young women all over the world, helping them to recognize the value of their life's calling.

An elderly woman, gray hair drawn into a bun at the nape of her neck, approached the front, supported by a gnarled,

wooden walking cane. I studied her African print caftan—
gold, orange, brown, and green—and her earrings, yellow
feathers dangling from each lobe. *Stunning,* I thought.

She began to sing, *a capella.* "Why should I feel
discouraged . . ." By the time she sang the lyrics, "His eye is
on the sparrow," I was mesmerized, my mouth wide open,
fan frozen still in my hand.

The service concluded with each of us filing to the front,
past the family, and out into the sunlight as the casket was
moved into the hearse. I stood there in the crowd alone,
looking for Dee. As the hearse pulled away, people
dispersed, arms around each other, hugging, then getting into
their cars.

A red Ford pulled up beside me, windows down. "Chile,
you need a ride?" Dee's warm smile eased the loneliness for
a moment.

"No, thanks anyway though, my car's in the back." She
was stopped in a line already stretching toward the swamp.
"You don't forget about those clues, now. Don't miss 'em,
that's where the livin' is, chile.''

She waved as the line moved on, then she was out of
sight. I heard myself say, "I know *that's* right, Dee."

I rounded the corner into the now empty back lot and
looked at my watch. Two fifteen. The service had lasted
three hours. Driving past the houses on my way back out of
the little town, I slowed to study the place where Mary had
spent most of her life. A woman in a rocker on a porch had
her hands in a large, metal bowl in her lap, a galvanized tub
at her feet. The toddler girl waved at me from the stoop
beneath her, cat still precariously dangling from her other

arm. A giant snowy egret perched on a cypress knee surveyed me from the swampy boundary between New Sarpy and the deserted highway.

CHAPTER TWO

I put my left blinker on to head home, although there was no one around to care which direction I chose. I wasn't ready to go back. Not ready to explain or answer questions that didn't yet have answers. I shoved the turn indicator up and headed toward New Orleans, opening all the windows, needing to feel the rush of wind in my face. *Needing to* feel," I thought. Lunch in the French Quarter, alone, seemed just right. As I turned off Canal Street onto St. Peter, I began to wonder if I'd ever had one of those clues they had kept on about. A parking spot opened up by Central Grocery. I pulled in, nose first. Didn't matter what size car I was driving, I still didn't have a gift for parallel parking and wasn't interested in learning.

The cell phone rang just about the time I had decided my parking job was as good as it could get, only an extra several inches sticking out in the rear. "Hey there." I tried to sound more casual than I was feeling.

"Everything ok?" Eliot asked.

"Just fine," I replied, suddenly aware that *fine* was my standard response when I didn't want to share details.

"Where are ya?"

"Actually, I'm just pulling into the French Quarter; thought it would be fun to have lunch here."

"That's quite a detour you took—bring me something, ok?"

"Sure thing." Knowing that *bring me something* didn't mean a souvenir, it meant some sort of edible treat.

"OK, then, you gonna be home by dark?"

"Close to it, probably," I guessed.

"Alrighty then, see you when I see you."

"That's a plan," I answered. And the conversation was over, thankfully. Exactly what I needed, no questions, no asking *why*.

Realizing I may be too distracted later to remember picking something up for him, I went into Central Grocery. A muffaletta from there was always a sure-fire home run. I stood at the worn green Formica counter, watching the round sandwich being assembled. First the olive dressing, then the cheeses, then the meats. Prosciutto, ham, salami. It was cut in quarters, wrapped in waxed paper, then white butcher paper. "Ya want a crème soda or a Dixie Beer ta go wit dis?"

I shook my head "no thanks." I glanced over at the long counter lining the wall, people on stools eating, probably locals.

Thinking I wouldn't be long, I tossed the sandwich in the car and rounded the corner at Jackson Square. A stiff wind was kicking up, likely that cold front I had heard people at the sandwich counter discussing. Pigeons scattered as I picked up my pace toward the little bakery ahead, passing the wrought iron fence surrounding the square. I looked up toward the steeples of the old cathedral, silhouettes now against a graying sky. Glancing back to my path, I saw artists packing up their works, removing them from the iron fencing, placing their palettes and brushes into canvas bags or tattered suitcases. It was Saturday on the Square, big business usually. This weather system would surely be a disappointment to those who painted portraits, told fortunes, or sold trinkets to support themselves.

Through the fence, I saw a woman huddled at the foot of a tree, near the giant statue of Andrew Jackson atop a rearing horse. The smell of fresh-baked bread quickly pulled my focus back to my reality: hunger. I loved this place with the French-speaking employees, white aprons, glass cases with Napoleons and tarts, baskets of baguettes, rolls, breads of all shapes and sizes, bowls of fresh fruits and salads. I ordered a cup of soup and watched as a hunk of crusty bread was placed on my tray alongside a pat of fresh butter.

From my seat by the window, I had a view of the woman beside the tree straight ahead. I wanted to digest the experiences of this bizarre day, take a deep breath, enjoy lunch, regroup, and get back to thinking about matters of the coming week. I thought it would be the perfect segue, sitting here—no one to interrupt my thoughts—but I was drawn to her. Finishing the last spoonful of soup, I walked to the register and heard myself say, "Soup and bread to go, please."

"Butter?"

"Yes, please. And hot chocolate," I requested.

Brown paper bag in hand, I stepped outside into the biting wind, arguing with myself. "What if she's not there? What if she gets mad and tries to hit me? Or spit at me? The "what ifs" flood continued as I walked through the huge gates and into the Square. In the distance, there she was, surrendered to the weather and her circumstance. Accustomed to the foot traffic around her, she never looked up as I timidly walked toward her.

"I brought you some soup and hot chocolate," I mumbled. I bent down and placed the bag beside her, struck by her lack of hygiene and realizing I was looking at her world, right there at the foot of that tree. She nodded, almost imperceptibly, as I turned and walked back to the car.

Opening the driver-side door, the odor of garlic was powerful. *The sandwich.* I wondered what *I* would smell like three and a half hours from now with the muffaletta as my passenger.

Heading home, I began to wonder if the nagging thought of the woman by the tree was some sort of *clue.* I thought about Pastor Henry's words about directions for what we need to do and the word assignment or calling. I was curious about what that meant, but afraid to consider anything so abstract or mystical. *Marching orders* is what my grandma used to call assignments. Probably not the same thing, though. I wondered if a good idea was different from a clue. But that nudge I felt hadn't come from *my* idea, for sure. Maybe I was always on such a roll, doing my thing, that I was missing these course corrections routinely crossing my path. Kinda like having blinders on, focused on what I planned to do. I thought hard, trying to remember any missed clues. By the time I turned onto Hwy. 190, it was dark, and heavy rain made it hard to see. Cars lined the shoulders, emergency flashers on. I slowed, passing them, wipers on high, trying to see enough to press on without further delay. I gripped the wheel as the flooded roadway caused me to hydroplane for a second. To distract myself, I thought about the women at the dance studio, each such a treasure to me. I felt my shoulders relax as I looked forward to being back with them at the studio on Monday.

I practically lived at the dance studio, answering the phone, spending time with the staff, enrolling dancers, planning events. The hours were long and being away for the weekend was rare. I loved it, all of it. I probably fit the description of a classic workaholic since my life revolved around the business. Eliot was a confirmed bachelor of thirty-two when we married. I had warned him that marrying a dance teacher with two small children meant an unconventional life from the git go. And now, with the kids grown and living out of state, my family of the heart was composed of adults and children whose lives had become so much more than business relationships to me. I celebrated with them and grieved with them. I was invited to birthday parties and weddings, and I never begrudged the long hours.

The women on staff had become a sisterhood, confidantes for one another and my role of mama or big sister filled a need I couldn't easily explain.

Karol was my best friend and business manager. She enrolled her daughter sixteen years ago and ended up as my right hand. Would I tell her about this crazy side trip? Absolutely. I imagined her giggling, probably saying she hated missing that one.

Leslie, who had been dancing with me since she was three, now a fine teacher. Always a team player, willing to do what was needed without wanting to be in the spotlight herself.

Lisa, also dancing with me since a toddler, loving ballet and now testing her wings as she taught what she had learned to the children. I'd been having her trained by Earleen, the seasoned ballet master on our staff, who gave Lisa notebooks full of lesson plans, equipping her to take over the advanced dancers. Lately, Lisa had been hungry to learn more, scheduling time to come in on her days off to be sure she was ready when the reins of the ballet program were handed to her.

Then there was Ellie, heading off to college soon; how far she had come from being a lost young girl whose mother abandoned her to move up north to be with her internet lover, and whose dad was then diagnosed with a terminal illness. We were family to her.

Brenda was the mom of one of our students. I pulled her in when the enrollment began to soar. Just last Thursday I met her in the parking lot and gave her a crash tutorial on how to teach a shuffle-step to little ones. She had never taught dance, but she danced in college. Her voice was sweet and even though she needed a lesson plan each week, I was grateful for her dependability.

Finally, there was Therez. A former dancer herself. She had called about enrolling her toddler daughter five years ago. We were having a growth spurt at the studio and I desperately needed another teacher. I had convinced her to come on board full time and quit her nursing career. We spent countless hours together this year as she became more and more eager to learn everything about how she could take on added responsibility at the dance studio. Because of her age, she hadn't quite adapted to our philosophy of always being age appropriate and conservative with music and choreography. I could see her becoming more understanding of that approach the last few weeks though.

Thinking of the studio crew made the stormy drive home easier. I looked forward to being back in my familiar setting, away from the confusing experience of the detour I had taken. If there were clues crossing my path, I'd like to think I recognized them. I would soon learn that some clues were missed.

I was exhausted as I pulled in the garage at home. Fortunately, muffalettas only improve with time. Eliot greeted me with a hug, saying, "You're mighty dressed up for driving home from Kelly's; do I smell Central Grocery?" I must have been reeking Italian deli.

More than ready for a warm shower, a good night's sleep, and a return to the life I had prior to that crazy day, I watched him open the bag like a child on Christmas morning. I felt the relief of normalcy return. I was home.

CHAPTER THREE

Betrayal never announces itself before coming to your home. It sneaks in, when you believe your closest relationships are real and you're singing their praises to the world. I was accustomed to storms this time of year, watching the radar to know if destruction was headed my way. Weather watchers offer advice when danger is approaching and the home front needs protecting. This storm had formed and grown into catastrophic proportion without anyone mentioning its threat.

The front doorbell was ringing as I was heading out the back door for Monday classes at the studio. Grabbing Isadora, our huge calico cat, I ran to the front where I was greeted by Chris, the guy who drives the brown delivery truck. "Bad time for me to show up, I'll bet," he said, extending the brown electronic clipboard with the dangling brown fake pen. I scribbled my name while he held the device.

Dance bag slung over one shoulder, keys in hand, cat under arm, couldn't imagine why he would suppose that. "Well, that depends, Chris, where's the box?"

"Miss Vicki, after all these years, even *I* know it's time for those costumes to start rolling in." He gestured with his head to an enormous stack of giant cardboard boxes at the foot of the steps. Reaching to scratch Isadora, he stopped mid-air as she hissed, her tail swishing wildly from side to side. "Where you want 'em?" He tugged the dolly with the first stack up the brick steps, three boxes, taller and wider than his six-foot ample frame.

"Right through there should be enough room." I shifted Izzy to glance at my watch. Chris had stacked the seventeen boxes floor to ceiling between the TV and Eliot's recliner. No way I could rearrange them before leaving. I locked the front door behind him, dropped the squirming feline, brushed the cat hair from my black leggings, and scrawled a sticky note to Eliot, "Sorry!" and stuck it on the remote control.

Cars were already pulling into the dance studio parking lot as I made my way down the tree-lined street and eased around back of the converted Victorian home, soft yellow with crisp white trim and glossy black shutters. The entry doors were painted candy pink, each topped with a black frilly awning edged in white piping. The staff cars were already lined up along the back fence, the vehicles as diverse as the women who drove them. I hurried past mini vans, compact cars, an old pickup truck, and a racy red convertible.

I entered through the main door, passing the sign on the front of the building, black with white lettering reading *Vicki's Dance Centers*, a color photograph of three young dancers beside the words. I paused to look at the fresh faces on the sign, each smiling at me. Remy, with long black pigtails, her Asian eyes twinkling; Sara, her blonde curly locks pulled back in a ponytail; and Ashlyn, her dark skin beautiful against her skirted pink leotard, hair pulled into a bun. This photograph spoke volumes about the business. The staff often joked to me that they felt we were the United Nations. Most southern dance studios seemed to be sharply divided according to class and culture, becoming extended social clubs for children's mothers, to the exclusion of those outside their circles. Having been raised on both sides of that division, I became intentional about changing the stereotype of *who* can be a dancer.

I entered the waiting room, already teeming with children and parents waiting for classes. Sunlight streamed through the long, uncovered windows, bouncing off the polished oak floors, illuminating moms helping with homework or chatting with those around them. Over half of the several dozen chairs were already filled. "Hi, Miss Vicki!" a chorus of little ones shrieked as they ran to see which could hug my knees first.

"Well, hi, y'all! How are you and your mommies today?" I stooped and made eye contact with each pair of eyes, moms and children, just about the time a chubby toddler decided to tackle me from behind. Losing my balance, I ended up at the bottom of a pile of tutu'd toddlers, each of us giggling hysterically, a few moms jumping up to help recover the contents of my bag, grabbing CDs and a banana and retrieving a lipstick rolling down the hall, Another parent extended her hand to help me up against the resistance of several little ones determined to keep me on

37

their level. I grabbed the purple migraine medicine syringe just before tiny fingers snagged it.

Through closed classroom doors extending from corridors off the halls, I could hear music as teachers prepared for their students; to my right, Tchaikovsky, and ahead to my left, *This Little Light of Mine*.

The office and dancewear shop on my immediate left was already buzzing, Karol helping to fit a pair of patent leather tap shoes on a tot clinging to her daddy. With one shoe tied, the satin ribbon in a bow, Karol touched the tap-shoed foot to the floor and softly said, "Tap, tap, tap, see?" Wide-eyed, the child released her grip, beginning to imitate the tapping sound, Karol stepped back and winked at the dad.

The toddler squealed a high-pitched, "Tap, tap, tap!" that echoed up to the high ceilings and into the hall. I gave Karol a thumbs-up and said to the dad, "Wait till she discovers we have another one for the left foot!"

"Miss Karol, I remember when I fitted *your* baby for her first pair of dance shoes." I walked around the desk and gave her a hug.

"Yeah, can't believe it's been sixteen years and she's about to graduate in a few months." Karol's Cajun accent was unmistakable, her round face and brown eyes set off by the hair color and cut of the week, ever changing. This week, an auburn bob. She handed the dad a receipt along with a silver candy kiss from the dish on the desk. "Bye bye, Ansley, see you tomorrow!"

We both watched the dad scoop up his little tap dancer, as he began to show her the photographs on the walls, children in dance costumes. "So, I'm reminding you about this weekend, our house, y'all are coming, right?" I asked Karol. It was Mardi Gras season and our house was on the parade route. Every year, we would have a party in our big front yard, putting the grill out under the giant oak tree to cook hot dogs, hamburgers, and sausage. I'd make chili for Frito pies and we'd always have King Cake in different flavors—apple, cinnamon, and praline cream cheese. Our wide front porch would be festooned with gaudy metallic purple, green, and gold streamers, and we'd haul all of our lawn furniture out to the front, often bringing extra chairs from inside. Sometimes our neighbors would rent big inflatable jumpy jumps for all the kids while the adults fried catfish and hushpuppies in propane cookers. "Remember, getting to our house gets tough close to parade time, so come early, ok? Tell Tim that Eliot will have his favorite beverages!"

"Sounds good . . . well, Kourtney, what happened to you?" Karol shifted her focus to a teen dancer arriving on crutches as the girl's mom approached me.

"Miss Vicki, I *told* her that the cross-country team may conflict with her dancing." I looked at the cast on her left foot, then at the dejected face above it.

"Want me to sign it?" I asked and winked, reaching for a Sharpie and smiling. The girl looked at her mom for approval, the woman gesturing resignation as I stooped to write *Keep on shining!* in neon purple marker.

"How bad is it?" Karol inquired of the frustrated mother.

One of the college-age helpers ran in and whispered, "Slight crisis in the main bathroom, we need you!" Waving to Karol, I turned to rush toward the scene, dreading the task before me, steeling myself to do whatever may be necessary. Easing the door open, I wasn't prepared for what I saw: a large empty liquid soap container on the floor, toilet paper roll beside it, also empty. The entire room had been papered, using the soap for glue. Sink, faucets, walls, toilet seat, door frame, floor, all decorated with white frills, the mirror done one square at a time, mosaic-style. "We may need to encourage the offender to take art class instead," I said, peeling the sticky border from the toilet tank. "I guess this will be out of order for a while; let's put a sign on the door and I'll get busy during the next class hour."

Therez brushed past me as I was standing on one foot unsticking shredded tissue from the heel of my shoe. "Hey, Therez! Don't forget about this weekend; bring the kids too. The weather is supposed to be perfect for bead-catching." Therez looked puzzled or maybe distracted. "Our annual Mardi Gras soiree!" I clarified.

"Oh, that's *right,* I almost forgot." She fiddled with her long, jet-black hair, then her bangs, checking herself in the oval mirror on the wall, stopping to get a bit of crimson lipstick from her teeth with fingernails manicured in the same shade. Her olive skin made her teeth appear almost unnaturally white. "Ok, I remember now." She glanced back at the mirror, adjusting the tight, red, v-neck halter dance top, tugging it toward her black spandex dance pants. "Who all is coming?"

"The whole gang, I'm sure. All of us, like usual; it's a tradition, right?" I watched her post a flyer announcing competition team auditions on the bulletin board. "Nice flyer."

40

"I'm going to personally hand-pick them this time," Therez said. "I want to be sure they're the right fit for what I have in mind. Choreography, I mean."

"Of course; want me to do my usual parent orientation?"

"No, I think I need to meet with the parents this time, let them know expectations for the plans I have."

"Sounds great, Therez, I'm always here to help." I reached in and shut off the bathroom light. I watched her move toward Classroom One, enter, and then close the door behind her. *She's strictly business at work,* I thought, reflecting on her words several months before.

*****

She had come by my house early one morning, excited about a piece of music she had found for the opening number at recital. I was affirming her choice, upbeat, G-rated lyrics. As I reached to examine the CD case in her hand, she gently said, "I told my sister the other day that I could never leave you, you've been so good to me. I'm living my dream, because you made it happen." Tears filled her eyes. "Before you reached out and believed in me, I, I . . ." Her voice trailed off as she swallowed down more tears. I had embraced her, knowing how hard it must have been for her to be so openly emotional.

"Honey, we are *family* and way more than just a business," I reminded. She squeezed me tightly as I continued, "Every dancer and their family knows they are

41

part of this crazy dance family too. What a great assignment, loving on all these people *and* teaching dance too!" I had smiled to myself, hearing the word assignment coming from so close to the surface of my thoughts. About that time, Eliot emerged from the bedroom, ready to head to work. Therez wiped her eyes. "Good morning, Eliot."

Eliot looked at me, then at her, then at me. "Alrighty then! Going to work so y'all can get back to girl talk."

*****

Since that time, she had gone back to strictly business, eager for me to teach her more and more about helping to run the studio and fill in the blanks of her limited dance training during weekly early morning sessions at my house. Each time, though, we'd share tidbits of our lives as our friendship grew.

"Costumes just arrived! Happy recital season, y'all!" I announced to the throng in the waiting room.

"Ohhhh, awesome!" shouted Ellie, a perky strawberry blonde with a bubbly cheerleader spirit. "I just love seeing all the costumes come in! Feels like Christmas!" Her enthusiasm was contagious, making her perfect for helping Brenda with the Tippy Toes classes. Her socks were embroidered with neon colored hearts, matching the stack of neon colored heart cut-outs in her hands. "And Happy Valentine's Day to YOU, Miss Vicki!" She extended a palm-sized card to me, then turned to greet one of her toddler students running toward her shrieking, "Miss Ehhwee!" Ellie held both arms wide, scooping up the pink tutu-clad toddler.

"Oh, Kenzie, I've *missed* you, it's been a *whole* week!" She spun around then tenderly placed the brown-eyed three-year-old down. "Now, let's go *dance!*" They skipped into studio two, both giggling.

I stood at the door watching Ellie gather little ones to sit in a circle, addressing each by name, telling them about a new princess dance they would learn that day. As she clapped her hands in excitement, eleven pairs of hands clapped in response. Brenda stood at the edge of the dance floor, memorizing the lesson plan for the class.

"Miss Vicki, I thought you were one of the teenage helpers standing there!" Chloe's mom whispered as she sent her into class. I glanced in the mirror across the room, realizing that my black tunic, leggings, and jazz sneakers caused me to blend with most of the dancers, even though being five foot two and a quarter allowed many of the tall, willowy ballerinas to tower above me.

The hall was lined with hundreds of framed photos and certificates, thousands of children pictured in costumes. I stopped to study a picture of Leslie in her first recital, long pigtails, cowgirl costume, gold-glittered tap shoes. "Now don't you get all sentimental, Miss Vicki." Leslie was beside me, clipboard in hand, heading down the hall to teach her four o'clock jazz class. She was followed by a single-file line of eight-year-olds in their warm-up jackets and capri pants, *Vicki's Dance Centers'* logo—a dancer in arabesque reaching for a star—printed across their backs. I thought of the legacy passed on to me from my mother and my grandmother, how I was the least likely of my pageant queen sisters to take over the dance studio. How I was the little chubby girl on the back row in my mom's dance class, never the star but savoring every second, and never imagining that I would be the one with the passion to create an organization that would grow to become the largest dance studio in the region. "I want to hear all about Celine." Leslie's voice trailed as she rounded the corner to studio three.

The halls were bulging with dancers waiting to be called into class, moms glancing at their watches, some wanting to head to the grocery store and some to happy hour. "I suppose I need to check the clock batteries!" I shouted to the crowd, moving toward the closed door at the end of the hall. I peeked in. Lisa and Therez sat in folding chairs by the window, stopping their conversation abruptly when I looked in. The wall clock read six after four. "Everything ok, y'all?" Each stood slowly, Therez whispering a word to Lisa, who brushed past me without a word. "Is she ok?" I asked.

"She's fine. Will you let my dancers know that they can come in now?" Therez responded curtly.

"Absolutely," I replied. "Competition Team, Miss Therez is ready for y'all!"

And with that, moms were free for two hours while their six-year-olds worked on their production number.

I watched Lisa walk toward Classroom Four, sleek black leotard, blonde hair drawn into a tight bun, teenage ballerinas for her Classical Ballet class following her quietly. I fell in step at the end of the group, walking into class with the dancers. I walked over to Lisa, touched her arm, and whispered, "You ok?"

"I'm *fine*, why?" She turned to the dancers lining up at the barre along the walls. "Michelle and Taylor, remove those t-shirts and boxers. This isn't hip hop class." The two girls rolled their eyes at one another as they peeled off the layers.

"Just checking on you. Reminding you about this weekend, darlin'. Parade party at my house. Bring your sweetie."

"Is Therez coming?" The two of them had become friends lately. She touched *play* on her IPOD; the dancers immediately responded, beginning their plié and port de bras series at the barre, their fluid movements corresponding with their breath, Chopin's Nocturne instantly transforming the studio to a hushed, sacred space.

"See you this weekend," I whispered, tip-toeing past Karol's daughter, Mia, patting her lightly as I passed.

"Now, let's mark the dance," Lisa shouted. Dancers assumed their opening positions and as the music started, gestures and steps were hinted, but not danced. Marking time was a common practice for the beginning of rehearsal. Lisa clapped the beats, making music for the marking. Instead of spins and turns, dancers slapped the back of their hand into the opposite palm, all in time together.

"Ok, here we go, full out!" The music started and they were all breathing in sync, muscles evident on the extensions, the brushing sound of leather ballet slippers executing the battements. Full out meant bodies and hearts were invested to the max, nothing held back. They held the ending, the time when the curtain would be closing. Then they stood still, waiting for the critique. I quietly left the room.

In the hall, one of the dads stood outside the bathroom door and pointed to the "Out of Order" sign. "Is this something I can help with? I have an hour to kill and I really don't want to sit in there with all those women." He gestured toward the waiting room.

I opened the door to reveal the child's handiwork. "Oh, Lord! I expected you to hand me a plunger! I'm on it, Miss Vicki, show me to the cleaning supplies."

I walked outside to survey the parking lot. Parents wanting to score the prime spots were arriving early for the next classes.

"Hey, Miz Vicki." I turned to see Samantha's grandpa sitting in his old blue step-side pickup, waiting for class to let out. His walking cane rested in the gun rack behind him.

"Well, hey there, Mr. Jimmy, how's life treating you?" I answered.

"Can't complain. Is it true, what I heard?"

"Don't know what you heard, Mr. Jimmy, but I hope it's good. If it was, then it's true!" I said playfully.

"Well, Miz Vicki, I s'pose it depends on how ya look at it. Are you retirin'?"

"RETIRING?" I laughed out loud. "Now, James Michiels, I know there are some days when I look older than I am, but that's about the silliest thing I've heard in a while! Where in the world did you get that idea?"

"Samantha said she heard some kids at school talking about it, how this was gonna be your last year. One of them was Ms. Therez's daughter. I told her it was kid foolishness—you know how they can make stuff up."

"Yes, sir, kids can surely get things confused. Glad we got that one straight. Did they happen to say I had a house on a tropical island with lots of palm trees?" I continued to laugh, loving the conversation with this sweet man. "Seriously, though, we both know I'm having way too much fun to stop anytime soon; set her straight, will you?"

"Glad to hear it, Miz Vicki."

His eyes shifted to the door and Samantha, running to the truck and hopping in, shouted breathlessly, "I got a Valentine, PawPaw, look!"

"Mighty purdy, Sam, almost purdy as you."

I turned to walk back inside, then looked back and waved as he drove away. *Retire? What a strange notion for anyone to suggest.*

Back inside, Karol was sharing a thick envelope of photos with a dancer's mom.

"Miss Karol, I can't wait to tell you the latest rumor!" She snapped her head up to make direct eye contact with me.

"What rumor?" she searched my eyes for a hint.

"Something silly, tell you later. What are y'all doing?"

The mom standing at her desk didn't give her time to respond, "Miss Vicki, I want to work *here*!"

"Well, come on!" I kidded. "The pay isn't fabulous but the people are great." I walked around the desk to hug Karol. Glancing at the photos, I saw the objects of the woman's envy. "We *did* do some pretty fun staff trips last year." Scattered across the desk were photos of Karol, Leslie, Lisa, Therez, and me at the beach on Cape Cod, on a cruise ship in the Bahamas, in New York City for the Macy's Parade, and in Las Vegas for a competition.

"I asked Karol how much it cost her for these trips, and she said you paid all the expenses for all of this; is that true? Oh, I guess that's none of my business, is it?"

I laughed and put my arm around the woman, "We're a family here. I love that we can take trips together and go to fun places."

"I'm officially putting in my application if you ever have an opening, ok?"

"Noted. I just figure we'll all be here having a good ole time together for the next couple of dozen years at least. We're best friends; it's a plus that we work together." I picked up a photo of the five of us eating pizza at sunset on a sand dune on Cape Cod, the Atlantic Ocean in the background. "Miss Karol, I wonder where we're gonna be off to next?"

Karol shrugged and answered the ringing phone, "Vicki's Dance Centers, this is Karol, how can I help you?" Her tone seemed flat, like maybe she was getting sick.

I stood behind the woman customer and mouthed a concern, "You alright?" She met my eyes and shrugged, then pulled out a schedule to provide details to the person calling, shifting her gaze to the paper.

Five hours later, it was quiet.

Walking back toward the office, I noticed the door to the classroom down the hall was partially closed, lights still on. The place was clearing out, the last dancers, parents, and siblings trickling outside into the cool spring night. Nearing the classroom door, I could see into the room. Lisa and

Therez were standing near the CD player over in the corner, deep in conversation, barely a whisper. Mia was stacking props beside them. "Oh, I was coming in to shut off the lights—almost had y'all in the dark back here, sorry! Everything ok?"

Lisa and Mia didn't move or turn toward the door. Therez responded, "Just fine! Good night!"

"Nite, y'all, see you tomorrow."

Well, that was weird, I thought as I passed the locked office door. Karol had already slipped out without saying goodbye, probably exhausted from a busy evening. Turning out of the parking lot, I drove past the front of the building. Through the open blinds, I could see them still talking, Mia appearing to be listening.

On the horizon, a full moon was rising. *That's it!* I thought. *Doggone full moon always makes people act a little crazy.*

Stepping out of the car at home and looking up, a wisp of a dark cloud passed over the moon and then it was gone. The shadows of the old live oak tree in the front yard stretched across the roof and down the driveway, backlit in the blue-white light. I stood there and took it in, the crisp night air, the tree, the moon, and the uneasy feeling I was having.

"That you, honey?" Eliot shouted from the next room.

"Yep."

"You hungry? I barbecued a chicken, it was such a nice evening."

"Not really, but thanks." With him working during the day and me in the afternoon and evening, Eliot prepared the evening meals most often, unless I got take-out on my way home. I walked into the den to give him a hug. "Oh, I forgot." The stacks of boxes were divided into two with a tunnel from the recliner to the TV. "Built you a fort, I see."

"Yeah, I feel like I'm six and maybe I should drape some blankets over these. Me and Izzy could pretend we're in the wild." He stroked the big cat as she shifted in his lap. He resumed watching a crime show and I walked back to gaze out of the kitchen window, looking at the moon and how the shadows of the giant tree now stretched all the way to the back fence.

CHAPTER FOUR

The parade route by our house was already buzzing, barricades going up to hold back the crowds and keep the kids safe, street vendors selling trinkets, lawn chairs put in place to hold spots, police motorcycles revving their engines for anyone who cared to notice. Outdoor cookers dotted neighborhood lawns, teens tossed Frisbees as children played chase. "Eliot, you think we could have asked for a more perfect day for our eleventh annual?" I looked up, not a cloud in sight.

"Can't imagine it being any better. Hard to believe it's been eleven years. These people know more about us than most of our family. You think we have enough chairs?"

"Well, let's count." I began to name the dance family: Karol, Mia, Lisa, Brenda, Therez, Ellie, and Leslie. Then all of their spouses and children. "Ok, I keep losing count. Most of us aren't gonna sit anyway." I anchored the purple tablecloths with packages of hamburger buns as Eliot ran an extension cord for the crock pot of chili. The ice chests were full to the brim to suit anyone's taste. Across the street, I could see the big propane cookers being readied for the catfish, the giant slide being inflated with an electric air pump.

"I'm gonna start the first round of burgers and dogs; those kids always show up starving." The patties sizzled as he placed them on the hot grill.

After filling bowls with chips, I sliced the brownies, still warm from the oven. I pinched off a bite and fed it to Eliot.

"Can we put those back in the house and hide them just for us?" he joked. He glanced at his watch, then at the crowds growing along our street. "If they wait much longer, they won't be able to get in."

"You're right, honey, I'll call Karol and be sure they're close." She answered on the first ring.

"Happy Mardi Gras, girlfriend! Y'all almost here?" I asked.

"Oh, hi. Well, actually, uhh . . . we're down in the Target parking lot. Uh, Therez's family is having a party here for the parade."

"Ohhhhh, well then . . ." I tried to hide my disappointment. "You have any idea about the rest of our group, Karol? It's getting close to time and we haven't seen a soul."

"Well, most of us are here, I think."

"Oh . . . well, y'all have fun. Maybe stop by after if y'all are hungry."

"Plenty of food here, but thanks. Bye."

I looked at the covered bowls of shredded lettuce, cheese, sour cream, diced onions. The festive plates and napkins and cups, the circle of chairs on the lawn. Then at Eliot, flipping each burger carefully. Sirens in the distance heralded the start of the parade, drawing shrieks from the crowd. "They're not coming . . ."

"Hand me that platter, babe, these dogs are done. Who's not coming? Well, hey! Perfect timing, Ellie and Leslie! Y'all have to walk a ways?" Ellie reached out to hug Eliot while Leslie placed a platter of pigs in a blanket on the table.

"Can't believe we're the first ones here!" Ellie hugged me warmly. "Whew, we had to park over by the zoo and that's quite a hike."

The familiar cadence of the Grambling University Band was close.

"Whoooohooooo!" Ellie shouted. "Eliot, need some help getting those burgers covered up?"

"Naw, y'all go catch some beads. I'll be in the backfield here, ready to feed the kids when they get here."

"Actually, honey, they've had something come up and won't make it."

"What? They get in a wreck or something?" he asked.

The first float was nearing us, a triple-decker with masked Krewe of Boogaloo in red-and-black jester costumes peppering the crowd with beads, stuffed animals, cups, and doubloons. Ellie grabbed my hand and pulled me and Leslie toward the throng. Instinctively, our hands reached up high, fingers spread wide, and Ellie began shouting, "Throw me something, Mister!" Wads of metallic beads and long strands of pearls rained down. Ellie dispensed most of her loot to the neighbor children near us, much to their delight.

I turned to see Eliot munching on a burger, laughing with a neighbor, waving to me and giving me a thumbs-up and pointing to the next float, aqua wigged mermaids tossing plastic toy fish.

During a lull, Leslie and I made Frito pies, layering the Fritos, then chili, shredded cheese, lettuce, onions, and sour cream. "Guess our crew waited too long to get here," Ellie commented.

"Yeah, guess so, Ellie."

"Well, they're missing out," Eliot responded, tasting a forkful of my concoction. He had an easy-breezy manner of rolling with whatever arose, rarely finding much to get worked up about. In my heart, I wondered if I had said or done something to offend someone.

I slipped my arm around his waist. "Now c'mon, honey, I need you to do bead-catching while I finish this off."

That night, I dreamt of Mary Washington. She was wearing a cotton-print summer dress and a concerned expression, saying, "Baby, Mary's still here with you, don't you be forgettin' that, you hear?" We were sitting on the levee, watching the river rising, looking like it could breach its protective barriers, or worse, that the earthen dams would break. Then she was gone and Eliot's alarm was blaring "Fur Elise."

Eliot and I hadn't had our usual after-action discussion following the parade. Too many clean-up chores to handle and rather short-handed on help, we both fell into bed leaving it all unsaid.

"How'd you sleep?" he asked the following morning, handing me a mug of coffee.

"Pretty good, I guess." I proceeded to tell him about my dream. "What do you suppose that means?"

"Weird! Probably means that you heaped too many onions on that Frito pie," he said, kissing me on the forehead

54

and heading to the porch to read the paper. I climbed out of bed and followed him, wanting more conversation but realizing that may not happen. Some of our biggest arguments had arisen over me trying to analyze versus him taking something at face value.

The fishing movie had been the worst. Filled with interpretations of symbols and meaning, I was eager to examine the story over dinner after we left the theater. I had barely gotten the ketchup on my oyster poboy when he reminded me it was a movie about fly fishing, catching fish, plain and simple, and ending with, "Sometimes, I think I don't even know you at all, when you can't even see a fishing movie without trying to make something more out of it!"

So I sat on the swing in my PJs, watching him read the comics, feeling one of us was mostly sane and it may not be me. I convinced myself that I was being overly sensitive. I wanted to tell Karol about Mary Washington, see what she thought. I wanted to laugh with the friends I work with, have phone chats, ignore feeling excluded, blow it off.

"Let it go, baby." Eliot peered over the paper.

"Let *what* go, Eliot?"

"Whatever has you stewing. Want to talk about it?"

"Naw, it's probably nothing. Silly girl stuff. I do want to tell you about a side trip I took on the way back from Kelly's, though." I had shifted the topic easily, not wanting to have him try to help me feel better just yet.

I watched him biting back opinion as I shared about the journey to New Sarpy. Finally, he couldn't hold it in any longer.

"So, let me get this straight." He leaned forward, glaring at me. "You decided to go to this place in an area you *know* isn't safe. *Alone.* With *no* cell phone service. To a *funeral* of someone you don't even *know*?" His staccato accusations knifed the space between us.

I felt scolded, sorry I had shared it with him. Had I expected him to be interested? Maybe help me figure out this whole clue idea? This is why I missed connecting with my friends. They would help me laugh about it, or tell me it wasn't wise. Lovingly. Not have me starting to cry, wishing I had kept my mouth shut.

He sighed dramatically and went inside. I watched a hummingbird hover over an empty feeder near the porch rail, regretting opening myself up to thoughts I didn't want to hear, and needing kindred compassion or, at the very least, acceptance. Or to be held and comforted while I cried tears I didn't understand.

CHAPTER FIVE

The next morning, I pulled on my pink sweatsuit and headed to River Falls, thoughts of the previous few days dissolving. Eliot had given me a brotherly peck on the forehead as he left for work with a short, "Bye." Unless I reopened the topic, it was unlikely we would discuss it again.

Crossing the Red River, I felt grateful for needing to add a second studio location. Renovating the old building in the historic district had brought its share of challenges, far outweighed by the benefit of seeing the expansion actually happening. As I reached the top of the hill, I could see Beau's red dually beside the huge building. He had been the best choice for a contractor, I thought, willing to tackle this project and having a good attitude about it, too.

I parked beside the truck and walked around to the back of the building. It had been a little over a week since I'd been over there and I expected to see the interior beginning to take shape. Instead, the entire back wall was gone. Not modified, gone. Jagged edges framed the gaping opening. From deep inside the building, I heard the sound of a power saw straining against something that seemed to render it useless. The interior was lit only by the sunlight streaming in through the many holes in the roof and, now, through where the back wall once was. I was only a few feet from him when he stopped, startled.

"Well, good morning!" He turned, smiling broadly, already sweating through his t-shirt. Muscular, tanned biceps were dusted with wood shavings. He pulled off the safety goggles to reveal eyes as blue as his faded jeans.

"Morning, Beau." I felt myself blush slightly, relieved I was in the dimly lit space.

"Notice anything different, Miz Vicki?" he teased.

"Only some natural air conditioning you installed, Beau." I smiled back at him.

"Well, we had a little termite issue."

"Termites? Beau, how can that be? That wall looked so sturdy, I can't believe it."

"Come, let me show you." He eased past me, accidentally brushing against my arm. I followed him into the sunlight, where he bent down, motioning for me to do the same. "This here was your foundation." He pulled a screwdriver out of his tool belt and lightly picked at the chunk of wood. I watched as it disintegrated into sawdust at each flicking gesture. "Those are some sneaky little devils, hiding up around your foundation, making little tunnels and eating away at something that looks real strong on the outside, until one day the whole durn thing collapses."

"Oh, Beau, now what? Does the whole thing have to come down? I can't afford . . . we're scheduled to have this ready by fall classes . . . this is really serious, isn't it?"

"Aw, now, don't you go to panicking. I've already had the inspector out here and it's not the whole building." As he continued to explain the fine points of the construction plan,

I looked into his eyes, realizing I didn't need to know the details. There was something about Beau that made me feel protected and safe, as though I wasn't fighting the battle alone.

"Beau, whatever would I do without you?" My voice cracked, sobs from the previous few days escaping.

"Aw, Miz Vicki, now don't you get all scared. I got this building thing. You take care of the dancing stuff, ya hear?"

I sniffed and nodded, embarrassed that he had seen me so vulnerable. "Thank you," I whispered, turning to leave.

"It's gonna be one *fine* studio, Miz Vicki. How 'bout you go look at paint colors on this lovely morning. Pick out something really nice for this ole beauty?"

I swallowed hard, gave him a silent thumbs-up and turned to walk to the car.

Getting back into the car, my cell phone message indicator was blinking, one missed call. Before I could check for messages, it was ringing, caller ID indicating Kelly. "Hey, sweetheart, is it a beautiful day over there?"

"Mom, I've been trying to call you. Where are you?"

"Learning the fine points of termites; what's up?"

"Mom, I'm *pregnant!* Due early October." I sat there, hearing Kelly tell every detail of the story, brushing the wood shavings from my sleeve, watching Beau chunking decayed wood in the dumpster, feeling almost giddy with the promise of a second grandchild, knowing that whatever challenges came up with the building, I could count on Beau to make it all ok.

Hanging up, I rolled all of the windows down and breathed in the cool spring air. I would paint the building the same as the Alexandria location, soft yellow. The color of the light streaming in my windows and onto my lap. And the color of how I felt after Beau's assurance.

CHAPTER SIX

I could hear the raucous laughter when I turned off the car. Earleen's ladies' tap group, the Dancin' Dames, were having dress rehearsal for an upcoming performance. The newest member enrolling at age seventy-nine, they were well past the hang-ups common to another age or to perceived talent.

Earleen had retired from owning her own studio and missed teaching dance but not the business end. Our relationship began when I asked her to emcee our dance recital and, twenty plus years later, she was in her element teaching women her age how to navigate growing older, dancing through their transitions. Only her silver hair, drawn into a classic chignon, hinted at her age. Her toned body reflected a lifetime of ballet.

Drawn to her classroom, I peeked in. Eleven women in red sequin mini dresses, support hose, and tap shoes stood less than a foot from the mirrored wall before them, having just donned false eyelashes for the first time. Through their hysteria, their comments ranged from "If my grandchildren could see me now!" to "Now I'm going to have to change tights—you know what happens when I laugh!" Tears streaked through pancake makeup as each tried to regain composure. Earleen clapped sharply, announcing, "Let's run through 'New York, New York;' first, grab your top hats and canes!"

"Ahhh, therapy!" sighed Iris, striking her pose on the back row. Her classmates clattered their way to their starting positions, right thumb and forefinger holding their silver hat cocked on the side of their heads, right elbow out to the side, cane extended in their left hand, tip of the cane on the floor, right toe on the floor, right knee bent. The adjusting and shifting to arrive at the opening pose resembled human dominos as each corrected her stance to mimic another. All of this before the music began.

As I turned to leave, Earleen shouted, "Miss Vicki, we'd love to have you come and watch us perform Friday night!"

"Count me *there!*"

*****

The marquee in the parking lot of the Moose Lodge announced *Bingo Night Tonight, special entertainment by the Dancin' Dames!* The fluorescent-lit room was filled with long tables banked on either side by folding chairs, each occupied by a marker-wielding bingophile intent on being the one to shout the coveted word. The ball machine resembled a commercial popcorn popper, the caller on the microphone up front pulling the next number from a small chute on the side. "B7! Beeeeee . . . seveeeeeen!" Collective disappointment filled the room as participants reached for sandwiches and drinks brought from home, trading halves of tin-foil-wrapped pimento cheese on white bread for chicken salad on wheat, reaching across paper plates filled with sliced homemade cakes and cookies.

Not spying our dancers anywhere, I moved toward the only other doorway. There they were in a narrow hallway, holding hands in an oblong circle, heads bowed. "Lord, it's the Dames. At the Moose Lodge," Earleen prayed, "and, Lord, we need you to hold our bodies together and help us remember the steps, and Lord? If we stumble, show us how to make it part of our dance. And don't let us forget to have fun, too!"

A chorus of "Amen!" followed by giggles, the clatter of taps on linoleum, and they filed into the room, lining up in front of the bingo ball machine. Across the room, Marilee's husband was in his wheelchair, CD player on his lap, ready to push play at the appointed time. Val's granddaughter dispensed hats and canes as Earleen stepped out of line to grab the microphone.

"Good Evening, Ladies and Gentlemen! For your entertainment, we have dancers of various ages and stages. We meet weekly at Miss Vicki's Dance Center for laughter and tears and encouragement. Sometimes we even dance a little too. Tonight, we'll be tap dancing to a medley of show tunes. Please welcome The Dancin' Dames!"

From the front of the room, I watched the faces of the audience as the music began and, one at a time, the dancers turned and posed to the front. Within thirty seconds, the entire room was echoing an off-key but enthusiastic rendition of "New York, New York," interspersed with hearty applause.

The show ended with "One" from *A Chorus Line*. A few rows of eyelashes were stuck to dancers' eyebrows and cheeks, adding an extra measure of joy to their expressions.

Throughout the hall, stiff bodies struggled to their feet for an extended standing ovation.

On the way home, I thought of all the things my family thought I should do when I grew up. On that Friday night, I couldn't imagine wanting to be anywhere other than exactly where I was.

CHAPTER SEVEN

Sunday afternoon, I drove over to the studio for the weekly inventory of supplies and review of the books. Expecting to be alone, I was surprised to see Ellie's little white Toyota. From the parking lot, I could hear music, "Jesus loves me, this I know . . ." Unlocking the door, I shouted, "It's me, don't let me scare you, Ellie!" The music stopped and a red-cheeked Ellie responded, "Hey there, hope it's ok, me coming in today. I wanted to get these props ready for class tomorrow." Behind her, I could see the floor covered with bright yellow poster board, piles of fabric and glitter. "And besides, I always feel better here." Her chin began to quiver as she reached for a tissue.

Ellie's mother had left the state a few months before to start a new life with a man she met on the internet, leaving Ellie to care for her terminally ill dad. They were evicted from their rent house and taken in by the neighbor across the street, "Miss Bonnie."

"Oh, honey . . ." I reached to hug her and felt her give in to the injustice and sadness of it all, softly sobbing against my shoulder. We sat on the floor and she updated me on her upcoming high school graduation. "I want to make it all better." I was crying too. "It's just not fair." Then I assured her that I would be proudly cheering for her at graduation, sitting beside Bonnie and Bonnie's husband.

The studio was her sanctuary, a respite from a world that was forcing her to grow up much too quickly. Because of the friendships of the women, it was my place of comfort too.

"Do you need any help from me today?" she asked. I was always amazed how she could put her circumstances aside and reach out to others.

"No indeed, I'm just doing my weekend chores, but thanks, sweetheart."

We walked together toward the office.

"I need to borrow the scissors, that ok?"

"Of course! We should have a pair in the desk drawer," I responded, flipping on the light switch.

The combination office and dancewear shop was a mess, papers strewn over the desk surface, file cabinet ajar. A leaking soft drink cup left a sticky trail down the side of the counter, ending in a brown puddle on the shelf beside the new dance bags. I stood there, trying to grasp what had happened, remembering how Karol had left without saying goodnight once again. *Bless her heart, I hope she wasn't feeling sick,* I thought, putting the cup in the overflowing trash can.

"Oh my!" Ellie exclaimed, reaching for the trash can and kneeling to pick up the remaining crumpled paper under the desk. Glancing toward the spill, she said, "I'll go find a sponge—or a mop—or maybe both." I continued to survey the room, closet door open revealing piles of new tights, shoes, and costumes all tossed in a heap on the floor. Ellie reappeared with mop, bucket, and sponge. Without commentary, she cleaned up the sticky mess. "There!" she said, "now, mind if I hunt for the scissors?"

"By all means." I gestured toward the desk drawer.

Ellie opened the drawer. "Whoa!" The drawer was stuffed with undeposited checks and cash, all crammed in there with the pens, paper clips, rubber bands, and ponytail holders.

"Here you go," I said, reaching in under a hundred-dollar bill and pulling the scissors out.

"Anything else I can do for you here, Miss Vicki?"

"Thanks, Ellie, I'm good. Looks like I have a bit of work to do." I watched her head back to her project and thought about when Ellie herself was a student at the studio, always an optimist, always considerate of those around her. I set about sifting through checks dated up to three weeks prior.

Ellie turned toward the door then faced me and waited.

"Yes?" I could tell there was something she wanted to say.

"I just wanted you to know that Miss Bonnie, the lady I live with, said if you ever need any part-time help, she's available. She's a school teacher and free on the weekends and after school. And she's really nice."

"Thanks, sweetheart." I watched her walk toward the hall.

Dialing Karol's number, I left a message on the voice mail, "Hey, it's me, checking on you, seeing if you're ok. Call me."

"Ellie?"

"Yes, Ma'am?"

"What's Bonnie's number?"

She answered on the second ring. "Bonnie, it's Vicki, here at the dance studio. Are you still looking for a little part-time job? Great, then, can you start right away? Are you by any chance free to come on over here today?"

Within an hour, Bonnie was sitting beside me, entering stacks of checks in the payment journal, filing the papers, and tidying up the rest.

"Thanks, Bonnie, for coming on such short notice. I'm thinking Karol is too proud to ask for help and it looks as if she sure does need it!"

CHAPTER EIGHT

The weeks leading up to recital were a flurry of costume distribution, program book deadlines, dance photos, and practices, everyone focused on preparing for the big show. Parents tenderly placed yellow-feathered chicken costumes, fairy wands, tiaras, and pointe shoes in their back seats beside baseball cleats and uniforms. In Louisiana, softball trumps dance for many, although some tried to straddle the two and do both. I prayed for rain a lot, hoping those games would be postponed til weekends when we weren't rehearsing for recital.

The office was filled with moms asking questions about hairpieces and how to handle jitters. Bonnie occupied the tiny back file room, keeping the paperwork current.

One Thursday evening after classes, Therez and Lisa approached me, asking if they could do a duet in the show. They said they had been working on a piece for a few months and really wanted to perform it. They said they knew I wouldn't mind. And they wanted to be the last number in the show. Although it was unlike me to approve anything for the show without seeing it, hearing the music, and especially previewing the costume ideas, I agreed. I suppose I hoped whatever had caused the distancing between me and these two women could be smoothed over. Or whatever I may have said or done to offend either of them would be healed by this gesture. I watched them high-five each other as they walked out to the parking lot.

That weekend, Kelly and I finalized plans for her baby shower. She would drive over with two-year-old Jilly the weekend before recital, have the shower at our house on Sunday afternoon, and stay over for the show. As she recited the guest list, mostly the studio family, I thought how much we all needed to be together in a fun, relaxed environment.

"Mom, are you sure you're up for this? I know it's crazy busy right now," Kelly asked.

"I absolutely am up for this; it actually sounds like fun. And it will get you and Jilly here for the show, which she will love."

"And any excuse to have petit fours from the bakery around the corner, right?" She laughed.

"Busted!" We both laughed and she promised to coordinate everything with Leslie, her high school best friend. Eliot, listening from the kitchen, met my gaze.

"What, Eliot?"

"I didn't utter a word!"

"But you're looking like you have a mouthful you want to say." Eliot and I had gone back to being friendly, silently agreeing to stay away from touchy subjects, recital season carried enough stress.

I spent the afternoon honing the program book dedication.

*This year's recitals are lovingly dedicated to my friend and cherished colleague, **Karol Chenevert**. Over 15 years ago, when she enrolled her daughter in classes, I had no idea that she would be the woman who would be a most significant part of my life.*

It started several years ago, this "Mutual Assignment." We needed someone to be at the desk for a very short time on Tuesday nights . . . someone warm, with knowledge of what we do. I hesitated asking Karol, because she was a busy mom, working many long hours already. I was thrilled (and surprised!) that she agreed! The journey began . . .

Over time, I've seen the qualities that are essential for the person holding her position: a passion for our purpose, which is far greater than just dancing; an understanding that each child and family member who enters our doors is a blessing to honor; and the greatest of these is LOVE! She pours her heart out every day and it is filled, in return, with warm hugs from children and a renewed sense of purpose. Although her resumé would have been impressive, these qualities transform her position from job to calling.

Although her daughter is leaving for college this year, she can know that there are hundreds of children (of all ages) who consider her their "other Mom," Sister, Guardian Angel and friend. I am truly honored to be among them.

Thank you, Karol, for being the example of doing whatever it takes to accomplish great things!

I love you!
Vicki

"Want to read it?" I asked Eliot, who was looking over my shoulder at the handwritten yellow page.

"Sure." He picked up the tablet and sat down on the kitchen window seat, not far from my perch at the counter.

I watched his brow furrow and jaw tighten as he tried to force a smile, handing the document back to me.

"What do you think?" *Damn!* I wanted to press a rewind button and take the question back. When I ask him that, he assumes I want to know the truth. Today, I wanted to hear, "Really nice, honey, good job."

He watched me brace against his brutal honesty and stopped himself. "Good."

"And if you said what you really wanted to say, it would be?" *Why was I doing this?*

"I would say . . ." He stood and walked over to me, kissing me on the forehead. "I would say that I wish I had the ability to see the good in people, like you do."

"What do you *mean,* Eliot?"

72

His words were measured. "I mean you appear to see people how you hope they would be, or how they could be . . ."

Before he could add *instead of how they really are,* I stopped him. "Thanks, honey."

He didn't press it. "Sure thing."

I wanted to blame him for the heaviness, dread, funk I was feeling and couldn't shake. I needed to be buoyed right now and his attitude felt like a heavy anchor. I typed the dedication, attached a headshot of Karol, and emailed it to the printer.

Kel and little Jilly arrived as Leslie and I were readying the house for the shower. I watched the childhood friends embrace, reminded that most think Leslie is my daughter. Her mother enrolled her in dance at age three and she never left. She and Kelly grew up dancing together, then shared high school years, staying close as they each married and became moms. Although she was a gifted dancer, Leslie never seemed to covet the spotlight. The satisfaction of seeing her students' accomplishments was her reward. Her four younger sisters each started in classes and danced until they graduated and moved away. Leslie was a favorite of dancers and parents, choosing to see the best in each child regardless of ability or appearance.

"Sweetheart, you look radiant!" I reached out to Kelly as Jilly ran past me, chasing Izzy, fleeing past us through the open door.

"So, we're having a *boy!*" Leslie clapped her hands then stretched her arms around us, Jilly prying her way through our legs to be in the center of the hug.

73

"I hope this doesn't overload y'all, Mom and Leslie, it's so good being able to have the studio family together for the shower."

"I agree, Kel. It's actually a great time, we all need to laugh and have some girl time." I stooped to scoop up the toddler at my feet. "And besides, I'll take any reason to have my Love Bug and her mommy here!"

First to arrive was Gigi, my red-headed momma, dressed in a bright yellow muu muu adorned with giant sunflowers and armed with baby shower games and a bag of entertainment for Jilly. She had made calypso hats for each of them out of plastic supermarket bundt cake platters, ball fringe glued along the rim. Handing Jilly a pair of maracas, they snaked their way in a makeshift conga line through the house, saying *olé* to each other, giggling more with each shake.

Shower guests arrived and joined the great-grandmother and two-year-old, now doing the hokey pokey in the dining room, shaking it all about, finger sandwiches, cookies and baby gifts in the center.

Kissing me on the cheek, Leslie whispered, "It's never ordinary when Gigi's around."

"Nothing about our family could ever be considered ordinary, darlin!" I responded, placing a bouquet of spring flowers on the table.

Gigi would pause putting her right hip in just long enough to welcome Lisa, Ellie, Brenda, Karol, Mia, Therez, and some of Kelly's school friends. Eventually, Jilly became absorbed in the bag of goodies, pulling out a Chippendales' calendar and holding it up for her mommy to see.

"Gigi! What is that?" Kelly handed Jilly a cookie in trade for the risqué photos.

"Well, it's a Chippendale calendar for you, honey. I got all but Mr. August to autograph it for you, see?" She flipped through the months, stopping at October, a chiseled and tan young man holding a pumpkin strategically. "Ahhh, Chad—he's quite the dancer."

"Gigi, where did you get this?" Kelly whispered. "Jillian, baby, want a sandwich?" Not waiting for a response, she placed food in each little hand, moving the bag of fun under the table, to be obscured by the tablecloth.

"Oh, I got it at the Indian casino; they came for a show there. They gave me a backstage pass because I volunteered to go up on stage and dance with them. I have a picture of that too, now where's my bag?"

And with that, the crowd moved into the family room, where they were all giggling, snacking, reminiscing, playing games, ooohhhing and ahhhhing over teeny nightshirts adorned with helicopters and basketballs.

After playing the toilet paper game, Kelly stood at the door, hugging the departing shower-goers, saying to each, "See you at recital!"

CHAPTER NINE

Over 6,000 tickets had been sold. Dancers of all ages would become stars for an evening. Every florist in town was inundated with orders for bouquets. Incoming flights bore grandparents from throughout the country. And I had an uneasy feeling that I couldn't shake.

The theater parking lot was already filling when I arrived. Family members carried armloads of costumes and makeup cases. Dancers in pink sponge rollers yielded to cars trying to secure spots near the entrance. Sheriff's deputies stood ready to intervene when needed. By law, we were required to have armed law enforcement for a public event of this size. I thought of previous years, dance family members getting into squabbles over seats, being stopped just short of hair pulling and thrown punches.

Backstage, competition team members were rehearsing on the unlit stage, marking through the line changes, chanting eight-counts in lieu of music. I watched Therez tip toe over to Eliot, press her body to his chest, and say, "How much do you love me?" I could feel him blushing as his eyes darted toward me, then back at her as she made the request for him to move a stage prop just before her ending dance. Her white teeth gleamed in the darkness as my husband nodded yes with the obedience of a little boy. I noted to myself that, if I ever needed Eliot to do anything at the studio, I'd get her to ask him. She hugged him tightly as a reward for his compliance, dropped the radiant smile, and moved on with her agenda. Clearly, I'd never mastered the fine art of feminine manipulation, but if I ever wanted to learn, I had someone nearby who was a pro.

Therez, Lisa, and Brenda had clearly given themselves starring roles in the opening production number, having the teams serve as their backup dancers. They practiced holding their ending pose, then I stepped onto the stage and asked them to gather into a circle for our traditional pre-show prayer. Mia and the older girls rushed to grab the three teachers' hands while two of the younger dancers held mine. Leslie and Ellie squeezed in beside me. I looked at the faces forming the massive oval encompassing the entire stage. Many had been part of this ritual for most of their lives. We bowed our heads as I thanked our maker for bringing us together, for giving us the gift of dance and music, asked for protection from injury, energy to sustain us through the show, and a heaping measure of joy too. As "Amens" dissipated, Susie, still holding my left hand, pulled me down to her and whispered, "I will miss you, Miss Vicki." I hugged her and said, "I can't wait to watch you dance, Susie!" I watched her skip to her lineup spot in the far back of the group and wondered if they were moving away or if her daddy lost his job. I glanced over at her dad, headset on, signaling for the houselights to be brought down, hoping I would get a chance to interrupt his stage manager duties long enough to ask. He pointed to me, indicating it was time. I patted him on the shoulder, thanking him, as he held the heavy, red velvet curtain back just enough for me to squeeze through to the podium and into the spotlight.

"Welcome to each of you who are here because someone on this stage is special to you." I looked into one of the six video cameras filming the event. "And a special greeting to you family members who aren't able to be here because you are defending our country or are separated by miles or illness tonight. Know that you are with us in spirit!" With that, I announced the opening number and the three spotlights converging on the podium shifted to the stage. The music boomed from speakers surrounding the roaring crowd as the curtain was raised to reveal the three teachers, Therez, Lisa, and Brenda, framed by dozens of dancers. I caught Susie's eye as she skipped to her spot near me. I gave her a thumbs-up and she responded with an attempt at a wink. I turned to her beaming dad and gave him a high-five. He leaned in to whisper, "Over 400 wanting tickets were turned away at the door. Fire marshall came to be sure we didn't exceed standing room numbers. It's all calm now."

"Wow, thank you." I looked behind him at the toddlers ready to dance next, Ellie holding one of them, reassuring her how much fun she was about to have. I turned back to the dancers on the stage, remembering how many of them had also been reluctant for their first recital.

Toward the end of the show, the high school graduates took the stage for their lyrical piece to "People Get Ready." Their soft chiffon dresses in purples, blues, and greens seemed dream-like under the blue stage lights. I stood out of sight of the audience but close enough to feel the breeze of their movement as they swirled past. I watched them turn their shoulders to avoid contact with one another as they executed sweeping grand jetes, taking in deep breaths as they faced the back, exhaling with pursed lips when they turned toward the audience.

"People get ready, there's a train a'coming . . ." It was Mia's turn in the spotlight; her moves changed from lyrical to contemporary as the music crescendoed. *"Now there ain't no room for the hopeless sinner, who's hard on mankind just to save his own. Have pity on those whose chances are thinner 'cause there's no hiding place from the Kingdom's throne."* It was a powerful piece, depicting the struggle of people who choose to go their own way versus taking the right path. The dance ended with Mia stepping away from the throng, exiting the opposite side of the stage proudly, as the other dancers tried to pull her back in the fold. The audience paused before exploding into applause.

I stood, captivated, watching the remaining graduates move toward me. I hugged each one tightly, knowing they would be journeying into the world and leaving the studio after this night.

The evening had been a flurry of hundreds of dancers moving past me, some stopping for a hug, but most rushing to costume changes or to family members waiting to congratulate them. The final number was Therez and Lisa. They were standing across the stage from me, in the wings, waiting for their music. When they emerged into the spotlights, I was shocked to see them in provocative flesh-colored two-piece costumes. Their movements were fluid and sensuous. I heard a couple of cat-calls from someone in the audience. I blinked hard, not wanting to believe these two women would so flagrantly violate our "clean and classy" studio code, the promise we made to every parent that we wouldn't sell out to the standards of the current music video scene. But there they were, hips in sync with one another, red lips grinning widely when they faced each other. And taking several bows for the standing ovation the competition team parents were giving them.

And it was over. I stood backstage alone under the glaring fluorescent lights. The curtain operator descended from the catwalk above the stage and said, "Nice show, ma'am." And he, too, disappeared through the heavy double doors leading into the night. Ellie appeared from the nearest dressing room, bouquets of flowers in each arm. Kelly and little Jilly were behind her, Jilly taking the opportunity to have the stage to herself, pirouetting until she became dizzy and landed on her bottom. I was suddenly really tired and fought back tears I couldn't name.

Kelly broke the silence, "So, Mom, I'll see you back at the house?"

"Yes, see you there," I replied, choking back my confused feelings.

"Miss Vicki?" It was Ellie.

I composed myself. "Yes, Ellie?"

"Thank you for this opportunity," she said sweetly as she reached to surround me with a flower laden hug.

"The pleasure is all mine." Her head rested on my shoulder.

She turned to leave, then turned back to face me. "Where are your flowers?" she asked.

"Mine? Oh, I guess I forgot to order me some." My attempt at humor was weak. She dropped to her knees and laid out every bouquet on the concrete backstage floor. Then she chose the largest and prettiest one and handed it to me.

"I'm sure these were meant for you and someone got confused." Then she scooped up the others and she was gone.

I allowed the double doors to slam behind me as I walked out to my car. Across the parking lot, I could see Therez and Lisa surrounded by dozens of families, all laughing and hugging and chatting under the streetlights. The test copy of the recital CD was playing in my car disc player as I drove out of the lot, "*People get ready, there's a train a'coming . . .*"

The back door was ajar when I arrived home. I could hear Kelly and Eliot in the other room. "It's not the time, Kel. You should know, after all these years, that tonight she needs to hear what was right. No critiques, even if she asks," he reminded.

"But it was disrespectful on so many levels," she replied.

I interrupted the conversation. "Hey, what'd you think, Kel? You haven't been to one of these in a few years."

She searched my face. "Beautiful?"

"And . . . anything else?" I prodded.

She turned to Eliot, who was shaking his head sternly as if to say, "Don't go there, even if she pushes, not tonight."

"No, Jilly couldn't stay in her seat. Once I had to chase her down the aisle; she was headed up to you on the stage," she offered benignly.

"Where is my Jillybean?" I asked.

"In the bedroom, in front of the mirror, dancing. Naked," she offered.

"Oh to be that free . . ." I said wistfully.

And the topic was closed for the evening, elephant securely in place in the center of the room.

CHAPTER TEN

The remainder of the weekend went without any mention of the recital. Even the telephone was strangely quiet, as was email. Quite a contrast to the typical barrage of glowing comments and praise from family members expressing gratitude for the efforts to make the evening a success. If I had chosen to discuss any concerns with Eliot, he would have likely asked me the lessons I had learned.

Outside, I pushed Jilly on the swing hanging from the old oak in the front yard as she kicked her bare feet high in the air and shrieked, "Higher, higher!" I could hear Eliot and Kelly giving one another an after-action account of the show.

As I continued to push the swing, I asked myself what I was to learn from that evening. I thought of the high school graduates and what a bittersweet time it was, the countless hours I had invested outside of the studio. The long stretches of time on the phone through the years with each of them and their parents. They lost loved ones, some of their homes burned, there were questionable grades at times, even life-threatening illnesses, while their parents struggled with their marriages and raising children and losing jobs. I was there, walking with them through it all. They had each become extended family. Often to the exclusion of my own children and spouse. So what was I to learn? Jilly exclaimed, "Nuff!"

and hopped from the swing, then ran through the front door and out the back, spied the dog, and took off to chase him.

I learned that watching these dancers go out into the world is hard. And sad. And gratifying. And anything else I could glean from that night was buried under the image of seeing these kids leave the stage to begin a new chapter.

"Hey there!" Leslie was shouting to me from the back kitchen door. "I came in through the front, brought y'all a picnic lunch." She looked so different than the night before, no makeup, wearing shorts and flip flops, a contrast to the formal dress and dangly rhinestone earrings for presenting awards on the stage. She walked across the grass, arms open to hug both Jilly and me. "I ducked out right after the final curtain, needed to get out of those heels." I searched her eyes for what was unspoken. "I wanted to say goodbye to Kel and Jilly before they headed back, too. She said they're leaving early Tuesday morning?"

"Yes, it's been so good having them here. Won't be long before a little brother arrives." I heard myself making idle chit chat. "So sweet of you to bring food, Leslie."

"Hope you like it. I made my special pasta salad with shrimp." She too, was sticking to surface topics. "The garlic bread is warm and the banana pudding is in the fridge. Well, I'm off. Enjoy your afternoon. A new season is starting, huh? I hear Therez and Lisa are having a special meeting for the new competition teams tomorrow evening. Should be a mob at the studio." She turned to leave.

"Yes, and it's Therez's birthday, so I'll be sure there's a cake and lots of birthday signs posted everywhere before people arrive. Therez and Lisa are conducting the meeting, said they didn't need anything from me, so I'll spend my evening with Jilly and her mommy." I watched Jilly climb the steps and disappear into the kitchen.

"Well, I'll be around if you need anything." Her words drifted off as she followed Jilly into the kitchen to give Kelly one last hug.

The dog dropped a slobbery tennis ball at my feet then ran halfway across the yard, expecting me to throw it. Instead, I stopped at the potted tomato plant outside the door and stooped to pull the weeds that were choking the long stalks. Seemed like only a week or so ago I had cleaned out around the plant. Yellow blossoms indicated where tomatoes were soon to emerge. I pinched off several suckers, new growth that didn't produce tomatoes and drained nutrients from the main stalks. I examined every leaf and not one tomato had emerged. By this time of year, we usually had several almost ready to pick for Eliot's first tomato sandwich of the season.

I went to the computer to make birthday signs for Therez, printed them out on colored paper, and stacked them neatly with a roll of tape on top. I'd get up early the next morning and be sure that every surface at the studio had birthday wishes for her: mirrors, doors, even the CD players. If she was working on her birthday, at least everyone would be giving her warm wishes. Karol would pick up the key lime cake on her way in—Therez' favorite.

First thing Monday, Jilly and I performed my ritual for staff birthdays: went to the studio and decorated the place with signs, tying helium balloons to door knobs, stair rails, chairs, and even the faucet handles in the bathrooms. On the way back home, I called Therez and sang Happy Birthday on her voice mail.

Around six, I called the studio to check on how the evening was going. Karol answered and let me know there was a crowd there and she didn't have time to talk just then. "No problem, just wanted to see if you needed anything," I replied.

"Not a thing, we're good—gotta run, bye," she responded. I could hear the bustling chatter in her office and I imagined everyone was still on a high from recital and excited about the plans for the coming season.

At around 8:30, my phone rang. The caller ID indicated it was Therez, calling from her cell phone. "Well, Happy Birthday, darlin'!" I shouted.

"Thanks," she replied. "Can you come over here to the studio?" she asked.

"Sure, now?" I looked at Jilly in her pajamas, holding out a book for me to read to her for bedtime.

"Yes, I'll meet you in Studio One," Therez said flatly.

On my drive over, I was prepared for our conversation. I assumed that there were some who tried out for competition team who weren't ready. They were likely families who had been around for years and it would be sticky, letting them down. I imagined that she wanted me to make those calls. And I would, although the disappointments were inevitable.

Only three cars were in the lot when I arrived—Therez, Lisa, and Karol's cars were parked side by side. I pulled up to Studio One's exterior door. I walked in singing "Happy Birthday" and gave her a bear hug and a kiss on the cheek. "How'd it go this evening? I'll bet you're tired; let's sit, how bout it?" I sat cross-legged in the center of the floor, and she sat with her back against the mirror. I waited for the audition after-action report.

Her face was serious. "I need to tell you something," she said.

"Ok then," I responded.

"I'm thinking about opening my own studio," she blurted.

I felt my mouth open but no words came out. Finally, I heard my voice say, "My goodness, I didn't expect that. Well, we need to talk about this for sure. I hope you'll change your mind, of course," I finally said, hearing my words, sounding so casual, trying not to feel slapped by her idea.

I watched her stare blankly at the floor, then at the wall to her right.

I looked at the birthday sign taped to the mirror above her head, the one Jilly helped tape. Then at the second hand on the clock above the mirror. It was 8:43. I could hear my heart pounding in my ears. For a moment I thought I might black out.

"Therez, have you shared this idea with anyone here at the studio? The staff or the dancers or the parents?" I inquired, trying hard to resurrect the businesswomen I was supposed to be.

She hesitated. "No, just my immediate family."

"Have I said or done anything to hurt your feelings? Surely we can work this out?" I searched.

A red balloon tied to the ballet barre began to slowly drift downward, hovering just above the floor.

"I'll tell you what, let's give this a little time and you think about it. After all, you know how much everyone here cares about you. You can't leave our little dance family," I suggested, attempting to smile and make eye contact with a gaze that refused to meet mine. "How 'bout we talk in the morning?" We both stood. "We need to work this out. Let me help you, ok?" She didn't respond. "How 'bout I call you around ten a.m.?" I asked, feeling myself beginning to tremble involuntarily.

She nodded and walked out of the room into the hallway. I turned toward the parking lot door, barely making it outside before vomiting in the flower bed beside the door.

I sat in the dark car, watching Karol, Lisa, and Therez leave, walking across the parking lot together, stopping to share embraces before driving past me. I closed my eyes as each set of headlights shone at me, then out into the street. I turned on the ignition, letting the air conditioning dry my face.

When I arrived home, Jilly was asleep in the chair, holding the book she loved for bedtime reading. I could hear Kelly in the shower; Eliot was dozing in the recliner, weather channel muted and providing the tropical update.

I scooped up the sleeping baby and settled into the chair, held her close, trying to absorb the peace, trust, and innocence of her age. She sighed as she shifted her head, pressing her soft cheek to mine.

Kelly walked into the room, smiled at Eliot, then focused on the TV. They were listing steps for preparedness in the event of a storm. "Prepare in advance" was printed on the screen. "Be prepared to leave" was next. "Don't wait till the storm hits to get ready" was next. She walked toward us.

"My God, what's wrong?" She stooped to look at me, then down at Jilly.

"Therez let me know she's thinking of opening her own studio," I whispered.

"What does *thinking of* it mean?" She pulled up the ottoman to sit near us.

"Don't know. I told her we'd talk in the morning." I felt weak, drained.

"After all you've done for her, really? I mean, you've spent so much on her, buying that exercise franchise to help her make more money, and I can't begin to imagine what all those trips and workshops have cost you." Her eyes were fiery. "Not to mention the time you spent mentoring her."

"Maybe it's just a random thought she's having," I responded.

"Oh, hey, honey, I guess I fell asleep. Looks like Jillian did too." Eliot had reached for the remote to hear the account of a storm that had wiped out an entire community, its survivors saying how they didn't take the prospects seriously and lost everything.

Kelly scooped Jilly up and took her to bed.

"You bring us some cake from the studio?" Eliot asked cheerfully.

I shook my head no. "Sorry," I replied.

"Well, damn, I have a sweet tooth." He stood and walked past me to the kitchen, retrieved the ice cream from the freezer, then turned to me. "Want some?" he asked.

"No thanks," I responded.

Kelly had returned to the room. "Some news, huh, Eliot?"

"About the tropical storm?" He gestured to the TV.

"No, dammit, about Therez," she said impatiently.

He squirted chocolate syrup on the ice cream. "Do we still have any of those sliced strawberries in here?" He was shifting containers in the fridge. "Ah, found 'em. Want some ice cream, Kel?"

"No, thank you." She looked at me, exasperated.

Eliot took a bite of his masterpiece then stood in front of me. "Want a taste?" He held out a spoonful.

"No thanks," I said.

"Eliot, Therez told Mom she may be leaving to start her own studio," Kelly said.

"*May* be? What does that mean?" He continued to savor his dessert.

Kelly updated him on the plan to talk by phone in the morning.

"So, truth is, we don't know anything for sure, right?" he said.

"Right," I said.

CHAPTER ELEVEN

That night, I had dreams of being in the ocean, far from land. I would hear Mary Washington's voice but I couldn't see her. "Baby, you been pulled out by one of them rip currents and you gotta learn yourself how to float. It may take you far out, but let it take you out. You gonna get out there in the calm eventually, so don't wear yourself out trying to fight nature; it be stronger than you. Now float, look up at the sky, and you will reach that calm place, and when it's time, baby, you can swim easy back to shore." I felt myself going under, exhausted. Then I surfaced again, awakened gasping, sitting upright in bed, drenched in a cold sweat. I could see Eliot's face on the pillow beside me, the moonlight streaming through the open drapes. He reminded me of Jilly, how he slept, totally surrendered.

I propped up and thought of a conversation Therez and I had a few years back when Tap With Tammy had opened. We both said how much we admired the integrity Tammy had, not to recruit students from other studios, how she opened her studio with class. I knew that if Therez did choose to leave, she would do the same. We had shared too much for her to do otherwise. My mind had worked it out, but my heart hoped and believed that all of this was for nothing, that by the time we talked at ten, we'd be back on track and moved past her fleeting idea.

Eliot left early for a meeting, then called me thirty minutes later. "Hey, someone I just ran into in the elevator said something you need to know." He sounded serious.

"Ok, tell me." I closed the bedroom door, not wanting to awaken Kelly and Jilly, who would be heading back home later.

"Apparently, this lady is the grandparent of one of your dancers," he began. "She said she thinks it's real dirty how those women at your studio have been scheming."

"Scheming? What does that mean?" I asked.

"She went on to say how ugly it was for them to have an ad for their new studio in your recital program book, trying to be so smug and cute and letting all of the dancers and parents know that you were retiring. And how she told her daughter how wrong it was, what they were all doing." He paused.

"All? She said *all*, Eliot? What does *all* mean?" I was trembling. "But, Eliot, I asked if she'd shared her thoughts with anyone and she said only her immediate family."

"Sounds like she lied to you. This woman said she has a building under construction and will be open by Labor Day."

Kelly opened the bedroom door and put Jilly on the bed beside me. She mouthed, "Who's that?"

"It's Eliot. Eliot, do you have time to repeat what you just told me to Kelly?" I asked.

"Yes, put her on." I handed the phone to Kelly.

Jilly and I went in the kitchen to fix her breakfast while Kelly sat on the bed, listening to Eliot's report.

She emerged from the bedroom looking grim.

"Kel, who is *all*?" I asked.

"I'm calling Leslie." She turned and closed the bedroom door behind her.

Within thirty minutes, at 9:05 a.m., Leslie was standing in my kitchen, arms around me, saying, "It's gonna be fine." While I didn't know what she meant, I tried to believe her. I had to know if she knew about the plan.

"Leslie, have you heard any of this prior to now?" I needed to know.

"They've never included me in their conversations, Vicki. So, it's no surprise all of this was kept from me. They've been having little whisper sessions since last August when you took us all to Cape Cod for that workshop," she shared. "But, it doesn't surprise me; I'm like your other daughter and it's no secret about my loyalty."

I thought back to that trip, how it seemed such a great bonding time, learning together and then playing too, eating pizza on the beach at sunset, chartering a boat to see the seals.

Leslie looked at Kelly. "You're heading out today, right?"

"Not on your life am I leaving now," Kelly stated.

"Good, then. I'm going to head over to the studio for a bit, start to get ready for summer classes next week. How bout I come back in a few hours and see how I can help?" She turned to hug me before leaving.

"Thank you, Leslie," I heard myself say.

Jilly came running in to grab the last apple slice from her breakfast plate, blew me a kiss, then she was off again.

At ten am, I called Therez. "Hey, Therez, I'm checking back in, hoping we can make a plan for you to stay, darlin'."

Her voice was flat and cold. "I told you last night I'm going to open my own studio."

"Oh, I thought you said you were *thinking* about it. Guess I misunderstood. So this is it, I suppose. I sure do hate that. I'll miss you, honey. I guess we need to make a plan for you to get me your keys, maybe drop them off at Eliot's office today?" I said.

"Today? What about summer classes?" She asked.

"I'm thinking we just need to call it done if you're sure you're leaving anyway. Are you sure?"

"I'm sure," she answered. And she hung up.

Within twenty minutes, the studio extension phone in the kitchen began to ring. Each call, a dancer's parent, apparently reading a script: "I'm calling to give you my official notice of withdrawal from your studio, effective immediately. Please cease any charges to my account." It was stilted and cold, no greeting or other conversation and not open to discussion, any of them. The voice mail had thirty-seven new messages within an hour, as I missed calls due to answering others. I attempted to break through to each by letting them know that we would kick off summer classes the following week as planned. At that point, I assumed I'd be replacing one instructor.

By noon, I felt as if I had been flattened by a steamroller, caught up in the scene from Jerry McGuire where two agents were vying for clients who were caught in a tug of war for their business. I unplugged the phone and crawled back in bed. Kelly brought me the cordless handset for the home phone; it was one of the competition team moms.

"I'm not calling to read you the script I was given, Vicki. I just want you to know that the whole town will be watching you to see how you'll respond to this. You've always been above board, setting an example for our kids. This community will be watching to see if you will walk your talk through this." And she was gone, leaving me with her attempt at encouragement.

I pulled the white comforter over my head to block out the sunlight from the windows, wanting to close the drapes but without energy to do it.

I felt a hand on my shoulder, someone sitting on the bed beside me. Stroking my back, then whispering, "It's all going to be just fine." It was Leslie.

I pulled the covers from my head and looked in her eyes, then those who stood behind her, Eliot, Kelly, and Jilly. Leslie believed what she was saying, it was clear.

"How, Leslie, how is it going to be fine?" I implored.

"We'll make a plan, starting today," she answered.

"How about I start with checking the studio voicemail?" Kelly asked.

"Ok." I responded.

About an hour later, I heard Eliot. "Wow, she's been a very busy lady."

I got up and saw Kelly extending a yellow legal-size tablet for Eliot to see.

I reached for it and saw two and a half single-spaced pages of names. Then she had Lisa and Brenda's names and numbers at the bottom of the third page. "What's this?" I asked.

"All of these," she flipped back to the first and second pages, "left the scripted message. Lisa and Brenda left their phone numbers and asked that you call them.

I called Brenda first. "Brenda, I'm sorry I missed your call. How are you?"

She made no time for niceties, responding, "Miss Vicki, I won't be returning to teach at the studio."

"Oh wow, Brenda, I'm so sad to hear that. What are your plans?" I tried hard not to sound devastated.

"I'd rather not discuss my plans. I just wanted to let you know," she said curtly.

"Thank you. Any chance you'll change your mind? We'll all miss you a lot," I inquired, assuming what her answer would be.

"No. Well, I need to get off the phone now." And she was gone.

Kelly and Eliot were now standing beside me as I dialed Lisa's number. The conversation was very much the same. No apology, no emotion, no gratitude for the countless hours I'd spent teaching her how to teach, how to tap dance, how to communicate with parents of dancers. She wasn't returning and she wasn't explaining.

"I forgot to ask them for their keys," I said.

"I'm thinking we may need to get the locks changed," Eliot offered.

"Yes, I'll see if Leslie can help with that," Kelly suggested.

"I need to call Karol and let her know we're doing that, so I can get new keys to her," I thought aloud.

Eliot and Kelly shared a glance at that comment, which I ignored. There were some relationships that would endure any storm and Karol was one of those, I was certain.

Karol's voice mail answered, and I left a message about getting new keys to her, asking her to call when convenient. That afternoon, she left me a message that she needed to take some time off and she'd be in touch. That made sense to me; it was an emotional time for her, seeing the family break up like this.

I plugged the studio phone back in and began to answer the calls, hearing the same words again and again, trying to break through to these people I had shared so much with, but the work had been done, a plan put in place and masterfully executed.

Late that night our son, Robby, arrived. Which would not have been unusual except that he lived almost 2,000 miles away. Hugging him, I had no idea the level of concern swirling about me.

"Thought I'd spring a surprise visit to see y'all while my sister is here," he said casually.

The next morning, Robby, the businessman, began to ask me questions. Could he see a copy of the employment contract so he could review the no compete clause.

"I don't have that," I responded.

"Where is it, I'll go get it if you tell me where to look," he offered.

"I never had anyone sign a contract, Rob," I said.

"Oh, I thought I'd sent you some sample contracts a few years back when we last talked about how smart that was and needed to happen. Maybe I'm mistaken." He seemed confused.

"You did, it was, I didn't, you're not mistaken. It was apparently a very good idea. It just never seemed necessary; we trusted each other, cared about each other, had each other's back, we were family . . ." I fumbled.

"Well, then, the topic of recourse is off the table." He sighed.

Jilly extended one of Kelly's magazines to me and climbed into my lap asking, "Read please?"

The cover had the words *What I know for sure* in bold print. "What I know for sure," I read aloud. "Nothing, absolutely nothing," I heard myself say.

CHAPTER TWELVE

"So, who have you not heard from, Mom?" Kelly asked.

"Ellie, Bonnie, and Earleen," I whispered.

"Mind if I call them?" she inquired.

I shrugged, looking down at the magazine in my lap. "Might as well."

I heard her talking in the other room but couldn't make out with whom.

"Earleen says she knew nothing and will do anything you need of her in addition to teaching her ladies. Ellie says she is so sorry and especially sad that she didn't hear anything and could have cautioned you. And Bonnie says she'll be there when you need her, bless her heart," she reported.

"We need to go to the studio, Mom." Kelly was buckling Jilly's sandals, then brushing the toddler's hair.

Following orders, I nodded and pulled on clothes and shoes.

We had barely gotten in the door when we could hear car doors closing in the parking lot. I turned on the office lights, sat at the desk, tried to steel myself, and waited. I could hear Kelly greeting someone outside.

"Hey there, Miz Vicki," It was Sheila, Jazmin's mom. I braced myself. She pulled up a chair to face me across the desk. "Can I talk straight up with you?"

"Of course you can, Sheila. I like to think we've been friends for the twelve years Jaz has been dancing." I thought back to the magazine cover.

"Miz Vicki, there's some real dirty stuff going on, as you know. And I don't like it one bit, especially when kids are being put smack in the middle of all this mess. I got a call from Therez personally inviting us to come to her new studio and you know what, Miz Vicki? That's the first time that woman has ever spoken to me, never even taught my child, and here she was acting like I'm her new best friend. How did she even get my unlisted phone number?" She stopped to catch a breath.

I waited for her to finish.

"So, I'm told you're gonna be shutting your doors because almost every one of your students has committed to going with her, thinking you're retiring. And I'm here to ask you if that's true." She leaned in, looking at me, eye to eye.

"No, Sheila, it's not true. Summer classes start next week." I tried to sound confident.

"Who's gonna be teaching? And will you have enough dancers to have a class?" She wanted assurance. "Because I can tell you for sure, we are not going to *Simply Dance*."

"I'm in the process of working all that out, Sheila. You know I love Jazmin and I love you. We'll look forward to seeing y'all Monday evening. Sheila, thank you for coming in." I stood and hugged her tight, wondering if Jazmin would be the only dancer left.

She passed Tiffany's mom, mumbling to her, "This isn't right what those people are doing, Deanna."

I gestured for Deanna to sit and she refused, handing me a CD. "This has some words you may need to hear right about now." She placed the CD on the desk and turned to leave.

"Deanna?" I called to her.

"Yes?" She looked back at me.

"Thank you." I watched her leave and waited, watching Kelly and Jilly taking down the birthday signs and decorations from the night before. I picked up the recital program book and thumbed through it and found Therez's daughter's picture. There she was, her name below the photo with the caption "Simply Dance." *So that's what they meant, I thought.*

Friday morning, both Kelly and Robby left for their respective homes. Kelly, beginning her sixth month of pregnancy, had a monthly doctor's appointment and Robby went back to his job and family. Robby handed me a printed set of pages entitled Employment Agreement and Covenant Not to Compete. "For your future staff." He winked, then hugged me tighter than usual.

Future staff. I weighed the words, seeing no way to assemble a team of competent and capable instructors and office managers. Not to mention *students.* It had taken years for the dance center to become what it was and I could see no possible way I could start over, much less have the energy to try to make it all happen again. So I did the only logical thing; I unplugged the phone and went back to bed.

Then it hit me. I had a second location almost ready to open. Another mortgage, based on students and staff that no longer existed. It was to be the dream dance center. Multiple classrooms, fourteen-foot ceilings, oak floors, multi-level ballet barres around the perimeter of each studio, a stunning boutique space with glass storefront on the main street, new parking lot. All within a restored historic building. I had spared no expense when reconditioning the mahogany-framed glass front doors, keeping much of the interior original brick structure, and installing massive mirrors on the walls facing the barres. The sound systems were state of the art, as was the temperature control.

Yesterday, I thought it couldn't be worse. Now it was. I imagined filing bankruptcy and having a lien put on our home. We would lose everything. My heart was pounding in my ears and I could barely breathe. I searched for the half of the anti-anxiety pill the dentist had given me when I had a root canal a few months back. I found it in the little tan envelope with the dentist's name on it. I was shaking, trying to fill the glass with water, seeing it splashing out as I washed down the drug. I imagined Eliot coming home from work and finding me dead, telling people he was still trying to figure out what the hell had happened. I was cold and hot. I grabbed Izzy and held her tight, scratched her under her chin like Eliot did, trying to absorb her laid-back, cat-like, aloof attitude. She fought against my grip, dug her claws into my forearms and leapt to the floor, leaving dots of blood as a reminder that she would choose when and where she would be held. I sat in Eliot's chair and rocked, wrapped in a blanket now streaked with blood, trying to soothe myself the way I remembered Kelly explaining how little children must learn. So that they don't depend on others to comfort them. *What a crock*, I thought. There are times when people, no matter what age, need someone to comfort them. Then I remembered that the ones I turned to, especially Karol, weren't available.

The pill must have worked; I was still rocking when Eliot came home.

"I figured you'd be at the studio," he said.

"Doing what?" I asked, hearing sarcasm in my tone.

"Is that *blood*?" He leaned in to check out the source.

I nodded affirmatively. "Izzy."

"Izzy, you mustn't hurt your momma . . ." he cooed to the feline weaving in and out of his legs, leaving hair on his dark pants.

I wanted to say that I wasn't the damn cat's momma and could use a little sympathy. I felt myself take a deep breath and decided I liked the dentist's pill.

"Want some sweet tea?" Eliot was opening the refrigerator.

"No," I answered flatly. "I'm thinking I need to take up drinking," I mumbled to myself, thinking he wouldn't hear me.

"Gives you headaches, remember?" He was walking toward me. Rather, he was walking toward his chair, which I evacuated.

He turned on the Weather Channel and lowered the volume a bit. "Looks like we are in for quite an active season." He studied the tropical update. "Look at that; I don't think I've ever seen so many systems lined up like that, have you?"

I ignored the question. I wanted to say, "Really, Elliott? Are we really talking about the weather when I'm dying here?"

He turned up the volume as Izzy jumped in his lap and settled in.

"Stupid cat," I muttered as I went to find the hydrogen peroxide and Band-Aids.

The following morning, the rain outside mirrored my mood. Eliot had left for work without even a mention of the absolute devastation I was experiencing. I supposed he had always seen me as one tough cookie, able to skillfully handle whatever was thrown my way without his assistance. What he had failed to see was that this cookie had crumbled and badly needed an ally.

I turned the wipers on high and the oldies station on the radio on low as the drizzle became a downpour. As I veered into the newly striped parking lot of the nearly complete structure, the Righteous Brothers began to sing "Unchained Melody." Planning to sit in my car until the deluge slowed, I turned the music up. I watched as the wind blew the driving rain in sheets against the new awnings, causing them to flutter. The lyrics of the music magnified how much I longed for someone to hold me and tell me this would all work out somehow.

Beau emerged from the side entrance and held up a hand for me to stay put as he ran to his truck and grabbed an umbrella, then sprinted to the passenger side of my car, motioning for me to unlock the door. He was soaked and smelled of summer rain and sweat.

"Good song," he said, running his hand through his dripping hair and reaching to turn up the radio. Just as I was reaching to turn it down. Our hands touched briefly as he yielded to the volume being lowered. The brief contact left my hand wet.

"I wish I had a towel to offer you," I said, noticing his t-shirt was drenched and stuck to his chest.

I have a change of clothes in the truck," he assured. "Sometimes I listen to that song when I go night fishing."

"Night fishing?" I asked.

"Most peaceful place in the world, out there on that river, just me and the stars and the music." He leaned back and smiled, wiping his hands on his wet jeans. "No matter what my day has been like, I'll put my boat in that water and it all just seems to fade into that big sky."

"I may need to take up night fishing, then." I watched as he imagined being in his special place.

"Maybe so. Everybody needs a place where their troubles don't seem so big, where they can see that their stuff is just a speck in the whole scheme of things and where nobody's gonna get in their way, ya know?"

"And how important is catching a fish?" I asked.

"Some nights I don't even bait my hook." He grinned broadly. "Hey, the rain's easing off; you stay put and I'll come around to get you."

I watched him step out, extend the blue umbrella with Chappy's Marine and Tackle in yellow letters, and open my door. He held the blue canopy over me, careful to shield me, as we walked into the building.

"Just a little more trim work and I'll be all wrapped up here," he said as he led me into the dark interior then snapped on the lights.

It was more than I had envisioned. I looked at our reflection in the huge mirrors, Beau standing slightly behind me, beaming. Waiting for my response. For only a moment I wanted the recent events to disappear. I wanted to go back to imagining rows of dancers wrapped in the symphony of violins and piano as the speakers in every corner encouraged them to see themselves as the grand dancers they would become. Beau took out his phone, pushed a few buttons and the room came alive with sound. "Unchained Melody."

"I have it stored on my phone so I can play it out on the river," he confessed. "I have you a Bluetooth setting on your sound systems so your teachers can do that too."

My teachers. There it was—my new reality.

"I'm going to go get some dry clothes out of my truck, then I'll give you a proper tour." He was back outside when the music stopped. I could hear the rain on the roof, coming down heavier than before.

I heard him changing in the new hall bathroom, his wet clothes hitting the floor with a soft thud. "We might want to consider putting some hooks on the wall in here," he shouted from the open door. "You know, for when wet contractors need to change their clothes?" He laughed to himself.

He used the word *we*, I thought to myself. "Yes, Beau, *we* need to do that, for sure."

He emerged from the bathroom buttoning his shirt, wet clothes peeking out of a plastic grocery bag hooked on his finger. "Hey, where's our music?" he asked. "Well, the sound of the rain is even better, maybe."

"Now the lights aren't hooked up yet in the other rooms, but we can see a little bit with the flashlight on my phone. Follow me," he instructed.

Beau led me through the rooms, proudly narrating every detail, speaking in hushed tones as if the darkness called for that. I stayed close so as not to bump into anything.

When it was time for me to leave, he asked, "Well, what do you think?"

"It's so much more than I imagined, Beau. Thank you."

"I'll lock up and you go on ahead and, here, take my umbrella," he said, extending it to me.

"But what about you? You'll get soaked again. And you need your umbrella," I fumbled as I walked toward the door.

"I'll get it back next time I see you." His words left no room for negotiation. I watched him turn and reenter the building.

The day before summer classes were to begin, I called Karol to confirm a time we would meet at the studio to give her the new keys to the buildings. Her voice mail answered, her Cajun accent requesting I leave a message. "Hey there, Karol. Hope your little break has you ready to kick off a new season—I miss you. Let's touch base so we can catch up and make a plan to meet at the studio tomorrow before classes begin. Call me, please?"

Next, I called Leslie to see if we could meet before classes and go over how things would run. She answered on the first ring, saying she would meet me at the studio at two.

The following morning, I had an email from Karol. It read: *Therez's sister has offered me the job of receptionist at her salon and I've accepted. I've left my binder on the back steps at your house, along with my keys. I hope you will be happy for me. Karol*

I forwarded the email to Kelly, who called within seconds. "Surely, you're not surprised, Mom?" she asked.

I tried to speak, but choked on the words.

"Mom? You do realize that Karol has been completely aware of all of this, right?"

"She would never keep something like this from me." My voice was barely a whisper as I tried to grasp what she was trying to tell me.

"Oh, Mom. I'm so sorry. But you need to let that idea go. She and her daughter were in the thick of all the planning and scheming. Had to be. And I know you loved her like a sister, trusted her more than anyone. But she's not your friend."

I don't recall saying goodbye to Kelly but somehow the call ended. Karol and I were best friends and, no matter what happened, we always worked through it together, often laughing about it later. I knew that, whatever the future held, I had a loyal friend in her. Through thick and thin, even if the studio fell apart, I believed she and I were solid. I refused to consider Kelly could be right.

I called Eliot. "Karol's not coming back."

"You sound surprised," he responded.

"I'll talk to you later," I said.

"Wait, what do you want me to say? It is what it is, you know?" He sighed.

"What am I going to do, Eliot?" I pleaded.

"Why don't you call that gal in Baton Rouge, the one that used to live here. You said her students at competition were terrific," he offered.

"And say what, Eliot?"

"See if she'll come teach competition teams," he said casually.

I wanted to say, "Like she's just going to drop everything and drive two hours each way to come up here to teach?" But I didn't. Instead, I thought about it.

"What do you have to lose by making the call?" he asked.

I found her number on the internet and called. She answered right away. I asked if she would consider driving in to coach our competition teams. We agreed to email our thoughts to each other by the next day. I would later learn that, on the day I called, she was going through a painful personal crisis and needed a new direction, no matter how radical. We agreed on a plan for her to try it for the summer. She would get to see her aging grandmother who lived here, in central Louisiana, and we would see how it worked.

I called Bonnie next, not wanting to approach her last minute but hoping she was up for helping. "Bonnie, I hate to ask, but is there any way you might be able to work in the office this week?"

"I'll be there," she responded quickly. I wondered if she knew Karol had no plans to return.

The next day, just before Bonnie was due to be at the studio, she called, hysterical and screaming. She had walked into the kitchen and found her husband on the floor with no pulse. He was gone. The paramedics and ER doctors couldn't change the fact that he'd had a massive heart attack. I tried to grasp what she was saying, thinking through the truth that he drove her to and from the studio and was her protector. And then I imagined Ellie, just having moved in with them, this man trying to become a father figure to her. It was unfair that she should lose another man in her life so soon.

Within a few days, Bonnie called. "I need to come back to work."

"Are you sure?" I questioned.

"Yes, how about tomorrow?" She sounded fragile but determined.

I exhaled. "Thank you. How are you?" My heart went out to her.

"We're not gonna go there," she responded. "Put me to work and keep me busy, ok?" she asked.

"Deal. I'll do my best," I responded.

Ninety-four students were signed up to attend that first day of classes. Three showed up. Two of the three were sisters who were transferring from another state. The third was Samantha, whose pawpaw had asked me months prior if I was retiring.

I sat across the room from Bonnie in the office, each of us avoiding eye contact with the other. Then she spoke.

"I've got your back, Vicki."

"Thank you, that means more than anything. And I have yours."

"Now don't look at me and make me cry," she said. Her world had fallen apart in a completely different way. We were both a pitiful mess, but in that office, at that time, we weren't alone.

That first week, ninety-seven percent of our registered students were absent. And I was numb. Too numb to play tug of war with children in the center of it all.

My mom called to chat. "Well, it's been days since we talked. I just assumed you were busy with the start of classes," she chirped.

I hadn't told her. "Well, I have been busy, lots of changes at the studio." I tried to sound casual as I gave her the cliff notes version of the events.

"Oh no!" she exclaimed. "Whatever are you going to do now? Do you think maybe you just need to shut it all down so you don't go into mounds of debt? Put the buildings up for sale? I know a realtor we can call." She was less than encouraging.

I repeated the words Leslie had said to me, "It'll all be fine, no need for you to worry."

"But you've just invested a fortune in that new building. Oh my God, this is just terrible." At least she was sympathetic.

"Well, I need to run. Can we talk later? Are you ok?"

"Oh, yes, sweetie, I'm fine. I have two front-row tickets to the cage wrestling event tomorrow night at the Indian casino. How about joining me? Have you ever seen cage wrestling?" She was excited.

"Can't say that I have, but we have classes tomorrow night . . ." I reasoned.

"Well, ok, I'll have another adventure with this wrestling thing. I'm wondering if the front row is available because you have sweat and blood being slung all over you if you're up close." She giggled.

"Well, I will certainly be ready to hear all about it. We'll talk in a few days, ok?"

After hanging up, I thought about how often I had been frustrated about her unmotherly wild adventures. Always curious about people and places, always a mental list of what she was yet to do. Samba dancing in Rio is still on the list, along with a topless beach. Not the typical mom, but soaking up every second as she barreled toward her nineties. In contrast to her, I became super responsible, in charge, and determined to be the stable one in the family.

Cage wrestling, I thought, knowing she wouldn't fret a second about the what-ifs surrounding me. Like Eliot, she probably thought I'd pull it together. Always had.

At the end of the week, Leslie and I met to scale back the summer schedule, leaving only a few classes, each with two to three students. We were getting our usual calls of families transferring to our area, so we limped into the following week. By early July, we had nine competition team dancers versus the several dozen who tried out and were chosen. And left. The high-dollar investment in the coach from Baton Rouge drained finances, but she hit the ground running, teaching those nine students—six on one team and three on the other—like they were the Rockettes.

I began making grocery lists for Eliot, so I didn't have to face the encounters with former students in the grocery stores. It had become too painful to see children run to give me a hug, only to be pulled back by their parents. Clearly, some sort of battle lines had been drawn and I was designated as the enemy.

With the scaled-back schedule, I was home more. Even Izzy would jump in my lap occasionally. Eliot, on the other hand, was in his routine and accustomed to years of me being gone every evening. The Weather Channel continued to proclaim that we were in for it and we better get prepared.

And then came the storms, delaying the start of fall classes. It seemed that every tropical system being born had been programmed to target the Gulf Coast, most heading straight to Louisiana. Samantha's pawpaw called and offered to board up the studio windows and Beau secured the new building. Surveying the studios with the awnings removed, sandbags at the doors, plywood covering all exterior glass, I wondered if I was seeing the future of the business.

The business. Such an odd term when describing what seemed like something very different to me. Yet, it was all being reduced to numbers. Numbers of students. Numbers of dollars coming in and going out. Numbers of people on staff. Number of people I could trust. Number of friends. Those last ones were currently zero.

Eliot watched "the cones" obsessively. First, the red cone, the projected path. Then the yellow cone, the COD, cone of destruction. He would tell Izzy where he thought the hot shot weathercaster would appear based on his interpretation of the steering currents, a sure-fire sign that area was in trouble.

"Oh, by the way, the usual gang will be coming up to stay with us until the storms pass. Heard from them while you were battening down the buildings," Eliot remarked during a commercial break, keeping his eyes on the television, stroking Izzy under her chin.

"The gang" were mostly from south Louisiana, all unrelated to one another. Fred, Eliot's former fraternity brother; Eliot's cousins from Thibodeaux and their St. Bernard dog, Catherine; one of my former dancer's moms who lived in a mobile home, along with her now-grown daughter, Andrea, and their cat. Eleven extra people along with their pets. We'd done this many times before, had a scare, then everyone would head back to their respective homes. This time would be different.

CHAPTER THIRTEEN

Bonnie had contacted the few students who had registered for fall classes, letting them know we were postponing the start of classes until the following week. She and Ellie would ride out the storm in Bonnie's little brick home across town.

Kelly called. "Mom, looks like Louisiana is under the gun, are y'all ready?"

"As ready as we've ever been, sweetheart, just don't let this throw you into labor, ok?"

"I'm such a whale, not sure that would be a bad thing," she teased.

"Well, you just have a few weeks to go, so stay calm, ok?"

"I will. I just checked on Gigi. She's checked herself into the hotel at the Indian casino until this passes. Says she has provisions in her bag in case she ends up being there for a while. Says Brenda Lee is supposed to perform tonight and sounds fired up about that. Who *is* Brenda Lee, by the way?"

"A singer from her era. So glad you checked on her. Let's talk after this passes, ok?"

"Sure thing, Mom. You have the studios all ready?"

"As ready as they can be, I suppose. I don't think we have much to be concerned about, up here in the middle of the state."

Early the next morning, our evacuees began to arrive with pillows, pets, and perishables from their refrigerators. It was squally, a sure sign we had something brewing.

"Eliot, are we still in the COD here?" Fred inquired.

"We sure are. It's picked up speed and the winds should be really kicking up by nightfall. Anybody seen Izzy?"

"She's probably found a hiding spot," I answered.

I was pulling out candles and flashlights as our refuge became a flurry of activity. The cousins inflated their air mattresses, pushed furniture aside to make room for pet kennels and food bowls. Cats meowed and dogs barked. The Weather Channel volume was turned up to compensate as we all listened to the prediction of a worst-case scenario.

"So, shall I place our traditional hurricane pizza order?" Fred asked from his spot on the sofa. Through the years, this had become a ritual. Sweep the Kitchen pizzas with extra jalapenos, hold the anchovies on one of them, no need to go over the details.

"That would be great, Fred. You going to pick them up?" I asked.

"Yeah, anybody want to ride with me?" he answered.

Eliot jumped up. "I'll go."

A while later, Eliot and Fred reappeared, large pizzas in hand. "The talk in the pizza place is that we may want to consider a little more storm prep," Eliot mentioned, reaching for a slice without anchovies.

"Like what?" I wondered aloud.

116

"Like tying down the porch furniture and surveying what could go airborne. Like making sure we're equipped to be without power for a while. People are taking this one seriously."

I thought to myself that they always say that, just to make sure people are out of harm's way.

With the last bit of daylight, between rain bands, Eliot went out back to secure the iron plant stands and patio furniture.

"Look at him out there, running around like a crazy man!" one of the cousins said, laughing, standing at the kitchen window. The others gathered to see Eliot running across the yard, waving his arms, then hitting himself on his face, neck, and arms.

"What is he doing, some kind of rain dance?" they roared.

Fred opened the window and shouted, "Hey, buddy, need some music out there?"

"Help me! There's a nest of red wasps in that plant and I've stirred them up. They've stung me all over!" Eliot screamed, peeling off most of his clothes, then using them to slash at the stinging attackers.

Fred ran out, grabbed the water hose and began to squirt Eliot head to toe, front and back. I hurried to the medicine cabinet for salve and Benedryl.

By the time Eliot came limping in, he was a mess, with very little skin untouched.

"Anybody have a cigarette?" one of the cousins asked.

"Now? You're asking for a cigarette now?" I was incredulous.

"To make a paste, with baking soda and tobacco, then put some tape over it. Draws the stingers out," came the explanation.

A handful of cigarettes surfaced from an unknown source and the first aid began. Eliot had poultices from face to feet and the Benedryl was making him drowsy.

"Don't anybody touch that fern," he slurred as he crawled into bed.

By eight p.m., the power was out, leaving us with no news, only the sounds of the roaring wind outside. Sheets of rain slammed at the windows, branches crashed on the roof with heavy thuds. There was something about the darkness and quiet that magnified the storm. So we defaulted to our hurricane ritual, gathering around the kitchen island on bar stools or standing, Fred trying to get the weather radio to work. Catherine scurrying to quiet the dogs. I lit the candles.

The cousins set about with a flashlight looking for the board game. "Found it!" they shouted from the hallway. It was another hurricane tradition, playing Balderdash by candlelight. With no weather information, we presumed we were in good shape.

I pulled the ice cream cartons from the freezer, along with a dozen spoons of assorted sizes. We passed the spoons out and dug into what was left of the ice cream before it melted in the freezer.

Fred reached for the mocha almond fudge. "Seriously? There's not even a spoonful left in here! Who saves this amount?"

"Ahh, that would be Eliot," I confessed.

By two a.m. it was quiet, and all settled in for a bit of sleep, hoping to resume life by daylight. I turned back the covers and there was Izzy. Snoozing under the white comforter. "I can relate, Iz. It's a good spot to get away from the storms." Eliot was sleeping peacefully, having had more Benedryl around midnight.

It was barely light when I heard the static from one of the cousin's laptops detailing what was known thus far. The newscaster used the terms biblical proportions and apocalyptic near the coast. I hurried to the front door to check the tree. The front yard was covered in debris, limbs, and shingles. One of our river birch trees was sprawled across the front porch. But the old oak stood proudly, pruned a bit, but intact. The rope swing had been tied to its trunk in the last-minute efforts to secure loose objects. The steamy air smelled of fresh pine. In our yard alone, every pine tree had been snapped off about two-thirds up.

Back inside, the cousins gathered around the laptop hoping for any news of their area. Izzy stood at the open back door, surveying the mess as another squally band came through with a downpour.

We soon learned that Fred's home and work were inaccessible due to extreme flooding, and it would be months before he could get back into those areas. "Want me to go with you to survey the studios, Vicki?" he asked. Eliot's stings weren't as swollen but he was still hurting all over.

I was grateful he was with me, getting out to move branches and debris as we detoured and dodged to get to the main studio location. "Of course, you're welcome to stay with us, Fred." I assured.

"Thanks, I've been thinking about it, and this seems to be the perfect chance to check a few things off my bucket list," he said.

"Whatever are you talking about?" I asked.

"Well, I have a list of places, national parks and such, that I've been yearning to visit, maybe buy some camping gear and take a long trip. The rest of the country hasn't had this storm, you know." He seemed to have thought it out already.

"Are you serious? Don't you want to stay nearby and monitor the cleanup process so you can hurry home when it's time?" I reasoned. I couldn't imagine being able to go on a vacation when life was so ripped up.

"Why would I do that? I'd just be marking time when I can take advantage of this time off. And, besides, I can monitor the situation from just about anywhere if I need to." To him, it made perfect sense.

The downpour continued as we turned toward the studio. "It's flooded, Fred, the street is really flooded. I've never seen it like this."

"I think you're sitting high enough in this SUV, let's press on," he advised.

The water covered the street side of the property and was several inches up on the front of the building. "Fred. do you think the sandbags handled this?" I nodded my head up and down, coaching him to the desired answer.

He wouldn't commit. "Well, we'll just have to wade in there and see. How about we see if we can go in the back door; looks like the property is higher back there."

I pulled in as close as possible to the back, dodging downed trees and trash cans, noticing a corner of the building had been knocked off by a falling limb.

We both had on sneakers and shorts. "I'm thinking we keep our shoes on; you've had some windows smashed up there and we sure don't need to get cut," Fred instructed.

The back classrooms appeared mostly dry except for a puddle here and there from a dripping ceiling. The windows allowed enough light to assess things. Then we walked into the rooms closest to the street and felt the squish underfoot.

"Uh oh," Fred mumbled. "Looks like we have some issues. See how this wood floor is already buckling and popping loose?" He glanced over at me for a reaction and I had none. Like the ground outside, I guess I was saturated so nothing else could sink in. It was just one more thing. It made sense that I should pitch a hissy fit, or panic, or wail, or something, but I couldn't feel a thing stirring up inside. I wondered later if that's how soldiers feel in war, their feelings all shut down so they can still think. It was like standing apart from it all and watching it, like it wasn't me or my stuff at all.

"We need this rain to stop. Soon," he muttered. "You have any towels?"

"Not a one," I said calmly.

The town was banged up and contractors were in high demand. South of us, things were so much worse. Blackhawk helicopters flew overheard, shuttling in patients from affected parishes round the clock; it sounded like we were in the thick of battle. School buses transported thousands to our town, all arriving still covered in the toxic soup of the flooding, separated from families and pets, their definition of home changed overnight. Babies were being bathed in metal washtubs in the parking lot of our local truckstop. And I couldn't give enough. Enough food, bedding, pillows, clothes, shoes, toiletries, first aid supplies, resources. None of it would begin to fix these lives forever ripped apart.

Hundreds of people walked the streets or leaned up against buildings, desolate and defeated. They seemed to crave anyone who would make eye contact and indicate without words, "I see you and you matter."

Schools and churches became temporary emergency shelters for all walks of life. The devastation had been classless, destroying not only lives but homes and jobs.

I felt kindred with the heavy sadness as though, through this storm, we were united in an unspoken grief. I could walk among these strangers without the need to force a smile, needing only to sit with them on the edge of their darkness.

Fred would check in occasionally, from Yellowstone, from Maine, from the Amish country. He sounded exhilarated, saying that someday he may want to be a park ranger. His job and his home were still not accessible, so he wasn't going to waste a second stewing about it, according to him.

It would be a while before buildings were repaired and dance classes would begin. As power was restored and repairs were ongoing, Bonnie manned the studio phone, calling to check on those who had registered. Bonnie's street had been flooded and she had been ferried for ten days in and out of her neighborhood in a little aluminum bateau boat. I had asked her if she wanted some time off.

"No ma'am. I need to stay busy." She was adamant. Ellie had started at a college an hour north of us. Bonnie's home was now empty and, according to her, too quiet.

It now was late September and Kelly's second child was due any day. I was on standby, ready to make the eight-hour trek to stay with little Jilly when it was time. Realizing I may have short notice, I had a bag packed and kept the tank as full as possible. Eliot knew that I would take off with little notice. Kelly's neighbor was on call, just in case I didn't make it in time.

CHAPTER FOURTEEN

The call came around lunch time, Kelly on her way back from the doctor who advised it would likely be the next day or two. "Mom, I'm concerned about how you're going to get here, with the roads all messed up."

The storm had devastated the path I would normally take to Enterprise, Alabama. "*You* deal with getting ready to have a baby, Kel. I'll map out a plan to get there." I had monitored the news, thinking I was fully aware of road closures and bridge destruction. Quickly making a turkey sandwich, I set out feeling totally prepared.

It was a warm, sunny day. Traffic was heavy, with utility trucks by the hundreds heading south, like me. About sixty miles from home, the road was blocked, an arrow directing me into the heart of Cajun country. Leaving the interstate, now driving southeast, evidence of the storm was everywhere. Huge piles of debris obscured homes along the bayou to my left. Acres of cane fields, ready for harvest, were flattened to my right. Winding through quiet neighborhoods, most front yards held concrete statues of the Virgin Mary, toppled and smashed beside mangled swing sets and webbed aluminum lawn chairs. Other statues had their broken parts stacked neatly near their pedestals, as though the owners expected to totally restore them to wholeness. A twisted sign, partly wrapped around a post, read "Let Us Dress Your Deer," with a phone number. The image of wildlife in drag momentarily had me conjuring up what a non-local might think of that advertisement. In this area, some people sidelined by gutting, skinning, butchering, or mounting whatever they could hunt, shoot, trap, or catch, then filling their freezers and decorating the wall above the mantle.

Traffic slowed to a crawl as bulldozers, dump trucks, and linemen made their way toward the next on the list. Every several miles, another roadblock indicated no through traffic.

Nearing the coast, the interstate looked as if a child had dumped his life-size toys, scattering them in medians and on the shoulders. Debris was hardly a fitting description for these remnants of lives everywhere. Then, once again, I was detoured off the main roads, into zones where National Guard were posted at every corner, coils of razor wire stretched for miles, providing yet another *No Trespassing* signal.

The trees left standing were stark, burned, stripped, and held boats, bathtubs, and bed sheets. Like the trees, most houses had been pushed and flattened, leaving only an occasional slab or jagged concrete staircase as evidence of what was once a vibrant community. Makeshift tents erected in front yards were the only homes for people who gathered around bar-b-que grills or helped one another clear property. Some people stood or sat alone, just staring. I wondered what it was like at night, no power anywhere, and not knowing when or if that would change.

With about an hour left before sunset, I realized I wouldn't make it to Kelly's that night. The hotels left standing had all of their windows blown out, shards of metal and glass everywhere. Exit signs were non-existent. As I crossed Mobile Bay, I knew it was time to get serious about a plan for the night and I was feeling very uneasy about my prospects. I wasn't prepared to sleep in the car, but that became a real possibility.

I exited, heading south, seeing some chain motels with lights and intact windows. One by one, I was turned away. Those that were open were filled with FEMA workers, insurance adjusters, utility repairmen. No Vacancy. After trying number four, a desk clerk suggested I check a town south of there, Fairhope, then made a call and found a room for me at a bed and breakfast inland. All of the others had been flooded, she remarked. She drew a crude map, said I had about seven miles to go and wished me good luck on the remainder of my trip. She suggested I take the scenic route, since the business route would be congested. *Scenic route* was about the last priority then, but it did land me right in the heart of downtown Fairhope at dusk.

Pulling into the angled parking spot in front of the Fairhope Hardware store, I rolled down my windows, somehow thinking my sense of direction would work better that way. The brackish breeze reminded me I was near the water. I was tired, wondering if I was imagining hearing music. Turning off the engine, I distinctly heard, "*You can't take that away from me,*" either Frank Sinatra or Rod Stewart, serving as background music for a woman sweeping broken glass out of a mercantile store. Two men knelt at the street corner, planting autumn flowers, yellow and orange. When I asked, they let me know that my destination was just around the corner, both of them smiling and waving as I backed out of the spot and rounded the corner.

The inn was on the next block, beside the community playground and next door to the local ice cream shop. Across the street, a pet shop.

The check-in desk had a view of the dining area and the courtyard beyond. I was greeted and led to my room upstairs after being told that, if I was hungry, I could have something brought to my room, or I could eat downstairs. We agreed that I would come downstairs to eat in a few minutes. From the bedroom window, I could see children parking their bicycles at the ice cream store, others exiting with cones. I scanned the shops along the street. Most were closed or under repair, signs indicating that they would reopen soon. The planting crews had moved to this street, pulling the battered and dead flowers from the street-side beds, replacing them with artistic designs of new growth. It seemed odd, almost frivolous, to focus on anything but necessity at a time like this. But there they were, prettying up even the tops of the trash cans. I watched their faces as they laughed and talked among themselves, envious of their camaraderie. A quick call to Kelly confirmed no baby yet and all was well with them.

Downstairs, a place had been set for me, near the window. A white-aproned man whom I presumed to be the cook or chef greeted me, "Evening ma'am. We have some gumbo made, how does that sound?"

"Sounds so good, thank you," I responded.

At the next table, a woman about my age was finishing her meal. "Hi there," she said softly. "Seems we're the only guests. Want some company?"

I gestured to the empty seat opposite mine, and she picked up her coffee to join me.

I learned that she, too, was from Louisiana. The Slidell area. Had bought and restored an old Victorian home when her husband was killed in a car accident. And overnight, the water had risen above her twelve-foot ceilings, and into her second story. It was a total loss. She had evacuated to a friend's home in Montgomery, but had overstayed her time there and was now looking for her next place to call home. Her friend had given her a few clothes, so she was travelling light.

"How long have you been here?" I asked, polishing off the last bite of cornbread, having shared with her about heading to Kelly's for the baby.

"A week," she said.

"A week? Why so long?" I didn't understand.

"Well, as I see it, I have a clean slate. All of the organizations I belonged to are gone. All of my friends have had to scatter. The thought of rebuilding the life I had sounds ideal but, in reality, it's impossible. And I can't be defined by any of it anymore," she said flatly. "And there's something about this little town that feels like the sanctuary I need right now. It's been pretty ripped up, so sad about their big pier and The Grand, but this is a place I'm not ready to leave. I may actually see if I can find a furnished place to rent before others discover it. My insurance company has given me a little money until we can settle up."

I didn't understand about the big pier or The Grand, only being here for one night. Climbing the stairs back to my room, I realized how much I had missed simple conversation and sharing.

The inn had prepared french toast early for me. I hoped to see my new friend before leaving, but I learned she was off for a walk along the bay and I had missed her.

"The bay? Where it that?" I asked the girl at the desk.

"A few blocks in that direction," she said pointing.

I decided it was worth the extra five minutes to see if I could tell her goodbye. The expanse of sapphire water, rimmed by a sandy beach and moss-draped live oaks surprised me, the unexpected beauty of it. There was no traffic, no one in sight except for a lone woman down at the edge of the water, tossing food into the air for the gulls, maybe a hundred of them, white wings against the brilliant sky. I stopped and watched her, her head thrown back and smiling, gulls diving down to her for treats. I wanted to know her name, give her my number, hang on to the one person in my life who had the potential to be a friend. But I turned around and headed toward the interstate, thinking how many dozens of times I had sped past that exit on I-10, never caring to notice the choice.

Out of habit, I picked up my cell phone to call Karol. We always shared things like this. Then I remembered what Kelly said, "She's not your friend, Mom." And I put the phone down.

I took the route northeast, rural and cleared, as the woman had told me the night before. She had taken it when coming south from Montgomery. As I drove through the southeast Alabama countryside, I felt as though I was leaving a new-found soulmate and not sure if it was the woman or the place. As I passed streams and ponds, seeing fishing boats tied securely reminded me that I was accustomed to being anchored to the studio, answering the phone, greeting walk-ins, being there with everyone. It was my safe harbor. I thought of all the things and people I trusted, and now wondered if any of my judgment was sound.

I arrived at Kelly's mid-morning, learning that her contractions had begun naturally so we would wait till it was time for her to head to the hospital. By that evening, baby Jack arrived into the world, nature delivering him easily with no medical inducement.

Only once did Jilly ask where her mommy was. "Mommy and Daddy went to get the baby," I answered softly.

"Ohhhhh," she replied, then began to set her little table for a tea party. She snuggled peacefully beside me that night, safe and happy, knowing she could trust that all was well. As I drifted off, I wondered what growing up lesson I missed. I wondered if working around children, I had become like them, believing the people around me were well-intended. I replayed the past several months and years, looking for when I should have been more guarded, more skeptical. More like Eliot, watching for the signs of trouble.

Two days later, Jilly and I stood in the driveway, waiting for Kelly and Hank to arrive with the baby. I wondered if I would have been able to make this trip had all of this not happened. That night, as Hank placed baby Jack into Jilly's lap, I felt grateful to be there for a moment in time so precious.

CHAPTER FIFTEEN

I called to check in with Bonnie before I got on the road to head home.

"I'm so glad you called. My tongue's hanging out from answering the studio phone. Can I tell you, it's amazing?" She sounded giddy.

"Bonnie, I have no idea what you're saying. What's amazing?" I asked.

"Like I told you," she drawled, "the phone has been just a-ringing."

"Who, Bonnie, who's been calling?" I prodded.

"People, lotsa people," she answered.

I was getting nowhere. "Bonnie, what do these people who are calling want?"

"You name it!" she said excitedly.

"Ok, Bonnie, now tell me what that means. Please." I tried to be patient.

"Well, the carpenters called and said they're done with all the work, and you should be good to go. The tree man called and said he's done hauling off the downed trees and branches. The roof guy says the repairs to the roof are all done. And then all those people wanting a job and classes." She added the last part as though it was an afterthought.

"Alrighty. You've been busy. Now, Bonnie, what do you mean about all those people wanting jobs and classes?" I tried to speak slowly and be specific.

"Well, I had no idea so many people were having to start new lives and deciding on right here in central Louisiana. Bless their hearts. Even the National Guard is setting up a big operation at Camp Beauregard, transferring hundreds of families up here. Lots of dance studios been washed away down south of here; they're calling us wanting to know if we have any dance teacher spots open. Bless their hearts. And, mostly, I've enrolled a lot of new students. And, girl, until those dance teachers started calling, I was wondering if you were going to ask me to teach a class or two. And I'd do anything, you know that, but that may not be in your best interest." She paused to catch her breath and laugh. Until now, I hadn't heard her laugh in weeks.

"Wait, Bonnie," I interrupted. "Are you saying we're having new students enrolling?"

"Well, that's about the biggest understatement I can think of." She shrieked and giggled. "You know that combination class on Mondays at 6:15 you had on the schedule? The one with only two students enrolled?"

"Yes, the one I was needing to close," I muttered.

"Thirty-one. Did you hear me? Thirty-one in just that class!" she boasted. "Want to hear about the others? And, by the way, how many are too many in a class?"

I tried to process what she was saying.

"And I told those dance teachers looking for a job that they would be real lucky if they got to work for you. Told

133

them I'd call them back when you were back in town. Miss Vicki?"

"Yes, Bonnie?"

"This is exactly what I needed, something to keep my mind off things, you know? I really need to stay busy."

"I'm so glad to hear that, Bonnie," I answered, my mind still tangled in the "Bless their hearts," and imagining Bonnie teaching a class of children. *Actually*, I thought to myself, *the children would love her*.

I spent a few minutes letting her know that each class had a maximum enrollment, and we may need to add some classes to be sure we didn't have any that were too full. Then she let me know the phone was ringing and she had to go.

As I readied the car to leave, Kelly's friends were stopping by to drop off meals, filling her freezer with enough to sustain them for days. I hugged each of them and thought how lucky Kelly was to have these people in her life, not having any extended family nearby. She seemed to have a solid support system. I would miss that in my life, having friends like that. I couldn't imagine that being possible again, with so many people seeing me as the opposition now.

I passed the Fairhope exit on the way back to Louisiana, wondering when I may have the opportunity to visit there again. Hoping I would. The eight-hour drive took twelve. As I walked up the back steps to the house, I missed being away already.

Eliot and Izzy greeted me, Eliot saying, "Another one coming, looks like the same path. What a season!"

I knew he was talking about a storm. "Wow. What do you hear from Fred? Anything?"

134

"Funny you asked; he called last night, sounded happy, just went to see the giant redwoods. Glad for the extended time to explore the country," Eliot responded as he kissed me on the cheek.

"Is he worried about his house?" I asked.

"Didn't sound like it. He said he never knew what he was missing, such a beautiful world out there. Said he caught a fish and cooked it right beside the stream on a camp stove. He checks in with his boss once a week and they're not even close to reopening. Can you imagine? He's that happy with practically nothing, just a little tent and a fishing pole. He called it the luxury of unscheduled time."

I looked around at our home, all of the colors I'd chosen, the furniture, the pictures on the walls. "I suppose he's figured out that being content doesn't have much to do with his stuff. Or his house. Or his job even," I said, almost wistfully.

"Or he's figured out what he can't control. Which is almost everything." Eliot turned back to the Weather Channel. "One thing's for sure, I won't be trying to move that fern again if this one comes our way." He gestured to the television and the projected path of the newest system.

The next day, I set up interviews with dance teachers relocated by the storm. Each one had the same story, they lost everything except their lives. They were grasping at the chance that they may be able to do what they love and make some money. They varied from just out of college to seasoned studio owners. Each had their own philosophy about teaching dance. Many told of the events as though it hadn't happened to them; they were detached, still numb.

Most knew life would never be as it was. Through the dozens of unanswered questions they had, each seemed resolved to living out the answers one day at a time.

I set a tentative schedule to have a few of the women trial-teach some classes. Because each prospective teacher had a different approach to instructing dance classes, Leslie and I met to develop a system, lesson plans, an employee handbook, defining every process. She agreed to mentor those who seemed to be a good fit, monitoring the progress of required skills to be taught, as well as deadlines for completion of each task. Because of her humility, she'd always seemed content to step aside when it came to running things. She seemed to have a gift for leadership and, before, we had not needed any of that: the accountability, the processes and procedures. Before, we had intuitively figured it all out. I trusted each staff member to be in the best interest of the students, the parents, and the studio. As I read over the Employee Agreement, complete with no-compete clauses, it all seemed so cold. But efficient, organized, and defined. I had Leslie and Bonnie sign their agreement first. Each gave me a high five as I presented the documents to them for signatures.

What Bonnie lacked in dance business knowledge, she made up for in heart. As we kicked off classes, she cheerfully advised new families that she was still figuring it all out and they fell in love with her humanity. And humility. She came in early and left late. And she related to their losses in ways most would never know. She held children as they cried, telling her about losing their pets in the flood. "Whiskers dwowned in the water and now he's in heaven with my grandma," one three-year-old sobbed to her. Her ample arms held and hugged countless strangers as she opened her heart to them all.

Some of the trial teachers had too much diva in them to look into the eyes of a child and encourage them, much less hear about their sadness. And we had to part ways. I'd never fired anyone prior to then, so it had to get ugly before I stepped up. One gal continually tried to stir the pot, boasting about all of her accomplishments, criticizing the softness of our approach, and me. She believed that it was perfectly fine to blow a whistle in the face of a child to get them to straighten up. Letting that one go was easy, and it showed me that I could become a mama tiger when it came to protecting those children.

Across the river, the new location was filled to the brim with smiling dancers in the storybook building. Everything there even smelled new. New walls, new floors, new wood, new paint, new people. A new business. I wondered if I would ever feel new, instead of empty and hollowed out.

CHAPTER SIXTEEN

By Thanksgiving, the Weather Channel in our house had been replaced by football. Ellie was home from college for the holidays, looking grown up as she helped me decorate the studios for Christmas.

"Forgive me for asking, but are we going to have a Christmas party this year after the parade?" It was a touchy subject and she knew it.

I thought of the parties in the past, all of the staff and their daughters or moms at my house. I remembered last year, decorating the house, cooking, all of us squeezed into our home, sitting by the fireplace, the tree decorated head to toe with photo ornaments of each of them and their children. Eliot had once commented, "are there any pictures of our real family on that tree?"

We had played silly Santa, the stealing game with gifts worth a few dollars or less. I had scored a little plaque that read, *Happiness is like a butterfly. The more you chase it, the more it will elude you. But, if you turn your attention to other things, it comes and lights softly on your shoulder. Author Unknown.* I was fairly certain that Ellie had brought that one, which I later placed on my bedside table on a tiny easel.

I looked at her and realized that, not only had she lost her biological family, she had a huge chunk of her studio family leave too. "Well, of course, we'll have a party, Ellie." I tried to sound like it was a given, even though it had been nowhere in my thoughts. I watched her smile broaden. "I'm thinking we'll do something a bit different this year, though," I fibbed as though I had it all planned.

"I was hoping you'd say that," she said as she clipped the last string of white twinkle lights on the frame of the studio windows. "I was thinking that maybe we can do something to help those in need, collect food maybe." She had given this some thought. "I mean, it's nice to sit around and eat and stuff, but if we got the whole studio involved, we might really be able to help some people." She had truly matured.

"I love that idea, Ellie. It feels very right, but what made you think about that?" I asked, watching her turn away from me and my question.

Then she faced me, eyes full of tears. "We had one of those food collections at my high school year before last. Hundreds of big grocery bags all lined up for delivery in the cafeteria on the day we got out for the Christmas holidays. The next day, two of those bags got delivered to me and my dad. We didn't have anything to eat, and if it hadn't been for that . . ." her voice trailed off. I held her as she continued through her sobs, "So I know we could really help some people if we get busy. I'll be glad to help get it rolling before I go back to school for finals."

Right then, I decided that Ellie's photo would stay on my family Christmas tree.

"And can I share something with you? It's confidential, at least until I talk it over with Bonnie." She lowered her voice even though there was no one around.

"Well, of course, is something wrong?" I expected this was some bad news somehow.

"I'm thinking that, after finals, I'll transfer to the community college right here in town. They offer the same courses and I wouldn't be piling up student loan debt. And, if you ever need me, I can maybe work a few hours here at the studios."

I felt myself exhale, but wanted to be certain this was the right decision for her.

"I just really want to be closer to family. Bonnie and . . . you. And I really love being around the children at the studio if you could use me." She had made the decision before now.

Well, *that's* my Christmas present." I hugged her again. I miss you, miss hearing about your days. But I want you to be certain this is what's best for you."

My usual Christmas spirit didn't show up that year. It seemed as if, in every store, I was met by my former dancers and their parents who had chosen to go to the other studio. What I didn't understand was the intensity of their behavior. The not speaking, the turning to avoid me, the pulling their children back. I stayed awake at night and obsessed during the days, wondering what in the world these people were told that would cause the meanness. And the answers never came. I replayed the last several months again and again, trying to find something I missed, some sign that people weren't happy. Something radical, something small— something, anything. I felt isolated and almost paranoid.

140

CHAPTER SEVENTEEN

The recruiting of our new dancers had begun. It became clear that *Simply Dance* and its people were intent on shutting us down. Their dancers were taught what to say at school, the parents had a pitch too. They'd all been put to work to market the new studio. I couldn't play that game, nor could I give it my energy or time. And I wondered how long it would take for them to let it go.

It was New Year's Eve and, as I stirred the black eyed peas and turned the cabbage down to simmer, I thought of how I'd held fast to this southern ritual, sure to do the right things to ensure a year of health and prosperity. I pulled the sizzling, black iron skillet from the oven, then poured the creamy yellow cornbread batter in, quickly sliding it back in the oven. Superstitions, making wishes, none of that had kept me from having life so radically changed this past year.

Eliot was asleep, Izzy in his lap, long before the ball dropped in Times Square on the television. I stared at the blank notebook page in my lap. I'd written *Resolutions* at the top in blue ink. I scratched through the word and wrote *Intentions* instead. Somehow, this year, the usual goals of fitness, nutrition, and finance had lost their priority. What I yearned for most were qualities which had no formulas: peace, happiness. I tried to imagine something concrete, an action goal to write. *Spend time in Fairhope, Alabama.* I stared at the words thinking how silly that notion sounded.

At midnight, the guns being fired a few blocks away caused Eliot to wake and Izzy to scurry to the bedroom. "What happened to firecrackers and sparklers bringing in the New Year?" he asked, yawning. "I can't believe more people don't get killed with that sort of revelry."

"Happy New Year," I said.

"Oh, yeah, Happy New Year. I'm going to bed, you coming?" He leaned over and kissed me lightly. "Not that I can sleep with all that racket."

"After I shut off the lights and the computer," I replied.

On New Year's Day, my mom stopped by for dinner on her way back from the Indian casino. "Can't let the New Year go by without our good luck food, can we?" She chuckled as she drizzled syrup over her cornbread.

She told Eliot how she brought in the New Year Zydeco dancing to Wayne Toups. "I didn't know you knew how to dance Zydeco," I remarked.

"Oh, I never learned, I just followed the rhythm of the music and the people and had fun. The thing about all that Cajun style is there are no rules, everyone's dancing from the inside out, like their spirits are dancing, not their brain. I grabbed a girl in a wheelchair near the dance floor, wheeled her out to the center, and we just held hands and I spun her around and around. The look on her face, that smile, she was free and happy, not being on the sidelines but right out in the thick of the dancing. Ahhhh, it was a fun night." She'd had very little sleep and never seemed more vibrant. "So what did *y'all* do?"

142

Eliot and I looked at each other and promptly changed the subject.

I watched Mom back out of the driveway in her bright yellow beetle convertible, toot the horn a couple of times, then she was off, her bumper sticker illuminated by her tail lights: *Life's too short to dance with ugly men.*

CHAPTER EIGHTEEN

The night of January second, Mary Washington appeared during my sleep. It had been a while. Or at least, I hadn't recalled anything of her recently. But this one was odd, and vivid. She had on a sky blue dress and she was beside a magnolia tree in full bloom. Almost like she was in a treehouse, surrounded by those blooms. She was leaning toward me, telling me to look in the Alabama classifieds, in the real estate part, right away. When I awoke, the memory was still clear. I scrambled to grab a pen and scrawled Alabama classifieds, real estate part, on the edge of an envelope in blue ink.

"What's up? Making me a grocery list? Add cat food, if so," Eliot requested.

"Didn't want to forget a dream I had, that's all," I replied.

"Ohhh, I see. Better add ice cream too. And tomatoes," he instructed.

It was Sunday; classes at the studios would resume the following day. Eliot settled in to watch the playoffs on television after lunch. I picked up the envelope with my notations on it and headed to the computer in the corner of the dining room.

In the search box, I typed Alabama classifieds real estate. A site at the top of the findings, Al.com, appeared to be a newspaper somewhere in Alabama. I clicked on the real estate link associated with that one, having no idea what I was looking for. The new rental listings appeared first and, at the top of the list, the following: *Modest Fairhope Bayfront cottage for rent*. Next was the amount and a phone number. I gasped, then began to jot the number below Mary's instructions on the envelope.

I could hear Eliot in the other room, "Sleet? Hey, I better go to the store at halftime; scrolling across the bottom of the screen says we may get freezing precip later."

"Ok," I shouted back to him.

I wondered how in the world I ended up on a web site with a Fairhope listing, first click. Then, holding the phone in my hand, I shouted, "How long till halftime?"

"Thirty seconds and they're about to try for two. Damn, didn't happen. That would have put them ahead. You have my list?" I heard him shifting out of his chair.

With the phone still in my hand, I went to the kitchen and wrote a short grocery list.

Eliot reached for the paper, looked at the items, and said, "How bout we make chicken and andouille gumbo when I get back?"

"Sounds good," I said, eager for him to leave. "Will you pick up the fixins?"

"Sure thing." And he was off. I watched through the kitchen window as he backed out of the driveway. Then I made the call. A woman's voice answered with a recorded message.

"I'm away from the phone right now, please leave a message after the beep," a southern voice said, followed by a quick tone.

"Yes, this is Vicki, calling about your cottage. Please call me when you get this message." I left my number and began to sweat, concerned that Eliot may be the one to answer the call. I carried the handset everywhere.

We put the groceries away, started the gumbo, and Eliot went back to watching the game.

At dusk, the phone rang, an area code 251 number. I hurried to the other room to answer it. My voice was hushed, almost a whisper.

"This is Donna, returning your call about the cottage," a sweet voice greeted me. She told me that the cottage was modest but clean. That she'd like a six-month lease. Then she asked if I'd like to see it. Said that she'd be ready to show it starting Wednesday morning, maybe late Tuesday evening, was painting some of the interior and would be done by then. I heard myself schedule to see it Tuesday evening, then I said goodbye and sat there looking at the phone, listening to the football game in the other room, smelling the gumbo simmering on the stove. And wondering how in the world I could approach Eliot and have any of this make sense.

I put a pot of rice on and glanced in at the television. Fourth quarter, two-minute warning. Tied up. Then an interception and the game was over.

We sat facing each other, steaming bowls of gumbo between us, silent.

"So, I had a dream last night," I said, trying to sound casual. Realizing how rare it was for us to sit across the table from each other at home, how awkward this felt.

"Uhhh huh," he replied, blowing on a hot spoonful.

"You've heard me mention Mary Washington before, right?" I was staring into the bowl of thick, brown liquid.

He nodded, picking up a hunk of garlic bread.

"Well, she came to me in my sleep last night," I explained.

"You mean you dreamed about her?" he clarified.

"Yes, well, sort of," I fumbled. "It was really clear, so much so that I wrote it down when I woke." I tried to make eye contact with him.

I watched him spear the last piece of sausage in his bowl, then dab the bread in the remaining liquid.

"She gave me instructions," I said slowly.

"Uhhhh huh?" He got up to get another spoonful of rice, then gumbo. "This is really good, don't you think?"

"Yummy," I responded, waiting for him to sit again.

"Did you feed Izzy?" he asked.

"No. So, Mary Washington told me to look in the Alabama classifieds, real estate section," I blurted.

"She did, did she?" I wondered if that was a sarcastic smirk or the bread he was still chewing. "So, did you?"

"I did, it popped right up, a cottage in Fairhope for rent." I hoped he would be at least a little amazed.

"Yeah? And? What did Mary say to do next?" he was trying to stay with me.

"Nothing, that was it." I answered.

"Oh, ok. Well, thanks for telling me about it." He stood, picked up his bowl and turned to put it on the counter.

"So, I called the number," I blurted.

He turned to face me, bowl in hand, direct eye contact now.

"And it's available to be seen starting Tuesday evening or Wednesday."

"Anything else?" He looked at me intently.

"No, that's it," I lied.

"You want to go see it?" he asked.

I looked at him, staring at me. "I do," I answered, not believing he was asking me.

"I'll see what I can do," he said, then walked in for the start of the second football game.

I sat there, shocked that the conversation had evolved to that point.

CHAPTER NINETEEN

It was a new year at the studio, classes were full, recital costumes were ordered, Leslie met with and mentored teachers, Bonnie ran the office. Ellie was growing into a competent and confidant young woman, able to jump in where needed. I stayed on the periphery, careful not to interfere with what was working.

During a break, I approached Bonnie. "I may need to be out of town for a couple of days, would that work for you?"

"Sure thing, we're good here. Always glad to see you, but everything seems to be rolling really well from my standpoint," she chirped.

I stooped to hug her, saying, "I'll see you in a few days then."

Eliot was in the bedroom when I got home, his travel duffle bag open on the bed. I felt a panic, seeing him packing, wondering if he was leaving me. "What are you, what is this, Eliot?" The breath was being squeezed out of me and I could barely speak.

He pulled Izzy out of the bag, replacing her with a pair of jeans and a sweatshirt. "Cleared my schedule for the next couple of days, so we can leave in the morning. Drive to Fairhope."

"Really?" I hugged him, although his arms were full of a cat intent on getting back in the duffle bag.

"Really," he replied. "Pack warm; nasty weather the whole way along the coast for the next few days.

The day was gray with a drizzle and occasional sleet. Bridges and overpasses were shut down with barricades directing us toward detours. We were already planning to take the inland route to avoid roads still closed from The Storm. We didn't talk much except about the weather, how the temperature was hovering around freezing and the roads could turn to ice. Even in early January, this was rare in the coastal South. I expected Eliot at any minute to declare this trip cancelled. We pressed on as a low fog hovered around us.

"Do we have time to stop for lunch?" Eliot inquired, "I need a little break."

"We do. I told the landlord we'd be there this evening and we'd call her when we were crossing the bay," I answered.

"How about Prejean's?" he suggested.

"Perfect," I replied.

Prejeans, pronounced pray-johns, was already crowded with locals seated at round tables around the dance floor. A band was playing a waltz, the singer pouring out the Cajun French lyrics of what sounded like a mournful love song. We were given a spot next to the band, on the edge of the dance floor.

Eliot leaned in and shouted over the band, "Correct me if I'm wrong, but isn't this Tuesday? What are all these working people doing, dancing on their lunch hour?"

150

The accordion player started a lively duo with the guy wearing a washboard on his chest. Diners dropped their forks, grabbed a partner, and began a counter-clockwise, two-stepping swirl around the floor. A woman in a Wal-Mart uniform danced with a young girl in a sweatsuit.

"Wanna dance?" Eliot winked at me.

"Naw, but thanks." I wondered when I had become so uptight, so serious, so unable to play. An elderly couple shuffled past us, both stiff from age but laughing as they made their way around the floor.

"They come here every Tuesday," the waitress offered, looking at the pair. "They always dress up and call it a date, split a cup of seafood bisque, arrive early, and stay late. Still in love at their age." She took our order and two-stepped across the floor toward the kitchen.

When it was time to leave, Eliot asked the waitress to put the couple's bisque on our tab.

"You're a good guy." I smiled at him.

"Try to be sometimes." He beamed.

As we crossed the bay, I called Donna. She was at the cottage, finishing up the last bit of work. Said we'd be the first to see it.

"Eliot, do you have any expectations of what this place will look like?" I asked, trying to soften what we may experience.

"Not really, what are you getting at?" he asked.

"Well, like there will be no furniture," I explained.

"No furniture? Well, how would that work, we can't afford to buy furniture." He sounded exasperated and tired from the drive.

"We do have a few things out in the back at home." I was referring to the workshop in our back yard. We'd converted it into a little apartment for when Kelly was going to a local college since that was cheaper than living on campus. "We have a bed, that old couch, your mom's dining table and chairs. A few things," I reasoned.

He let out a long sigh.

"They used the word modest in the advertisement and that could mean many things." I wanted to prepare him for whatever was ahead. "And for the money they're asking, it surely can't be fabulous, I'm thinking." I had already reminded him on the way over that we had a little money in the account from when we sold the camp, a run-down mobile home out on a local lake. We'd thought it would be a great getaway, but it turned out to be rat-infested and falling down. We were amazed when someone bought it "as is," putting an end to us having a little escape. And giving us a little profit to boot.

We arrived at the cottage at dark. Eliot wasn't able to tell much about the town or see anything on the way in, not even the bay. Donna's directions were vague and we passed the place several times before calling her. She stood out by the street and signaled us finally.

As we walked up the front porch steps, the peeling paint on the door frame was evident, even in the dark. It was freezing inside. Donna commented that the heater repairman was coming in the morning. As we walked from room to room, I avoided eye contact with Eliot. The kitchen had a small refrigerator and a stove, thankfully.

"No dishwasher?" Eliot whined, looking into the stained and chipped porcelain sink. He turned to face me and said, "Really?"

"Donna, thanks, we have a reservation at the motel down the street; can we have until in the morning to let you know?" I asked.

"The first showing is at eight a.m.," she said. "I'll need to know before then."

Until that night, I truly didn't know how desperately I wanted to be anywhere except central Louisiana. Nothing Donna could have shown me would have been a deal-breaker. I searched for a way to explain that to Eliot, but nothing I considered sounded rational.

Before checking in, we stopped at the local oyster restaurant on the same street as the cottage, a few blocks away. Our server, Sandra, had lived in Fairhope all her life.

"Why didn't you leave here, see the world a bit?" Eliot made small talk with Sandra as she poured our sweet tea.

"Why would I do that when I live in paradise, the most beautiful place in all the world?" she replied with a slow drawl, smiling at Eliot.

"Well, I've never been here before; all I can see is darkness and rain," Eliot complained. "I drove hours to come over here and look at some dump for rent down the street on the bay."

"There's a place for rent on the bayfront? My sister and her husband have been asking me to find them a spot, where is it? There's never a place for rent, only houses for sale for a million or more. Is there a sign? I'll call my sister and get her down here from Auburn tomorrow."

"Well, it's nothing special," Eliot responded.

"Honey, if it's on the bay, that's plenty special right there."

The diners across the room signaled her about then, leaving me wide-eyed and wondering how Sandra's words had impacted Eliot.

"Paradise? Plenty special?" Eliot mocked. "You're wanting to go for it, aren't you?"

"Yes," I answered, careful not to say too much.

"Alright, let's call the woman before Sandra's sister beats us to it." He sighed.

CHAPTER TWENTY

By the next Friday, ten days after we had given Donna the deposit and first month's rent on the little cottage, we had a UHaul containing random cast asides from the little apartment in our back yard. A sparse amount of furniture, some old sheets and a blanket, pillows, three chipped coffee mugs, assorted chipped plates and plastic mardi gras cups, an ice cube tray, a handful of mismatched forks and knives, a toaster which, like its sidekick coffeemaker, had broken power buttons but would work by plugging and unplugging them. The thirteen-inch tv would require a bit more perhaps. The old iron freestanding yard swing fit nicely and we loaded my old bicycle in case I wanted to go anywhere until Eliot would come back to pick me up the following weekend. I had pulled some staples from the pantry and the refrigerator and stuck them on my back seat, along with assorted clothes. I grabbed a flashlight, extension cord, and lamp as an afterthought, along with a bag of tea lights left over from Christmas.

Following the UHaul, I turned on the radio, hoping to dissolve the doubts and drown out the incessant *no signal* beeping of my cell. Thankfully, Kelly and I had made a plan. She, Hank, and the kids would drive down from Enterprise and meet us just after lunch. Hank would help unload the

155

truck and they would head back home that evening. For the hundredth time, she posed the question, "Mom, you sure you want to *do* this?" I found a station that didn't produce static, some guy singing about living like you were dying.

In front of me, Eliot signaled an exit at Diamondhead, Mississippi. I followed suit, slowing, wondering if anything was left intact this close to the coast. Passing the skeleton of what was once perhaps a motel, I dodged twisted metal, a shredded billboard proclaiming, "Best Bar B Que Ribs Anywhere!"

He hesitated, first a left blinker, then a right. *Probably not the direction of civilization,* I thought. Up ahead, I could see the remnants of a neighborhood, bare slabs swept clean. The truck stopped. I watched him step down from the cab, wiping his eyes. "What's *wrong?"* I shouted, leaving my door open as I approached him.

"Damn country music. It's the only station that has a signal. You have any Kleenex?"

Behind him, a wooded area distracted me. High up in the trees, a jet ski perched beside a yellow Jacuzzi tub. Stark branches snagged shredded bed sheets flapping in the stiff wind. A lone gull circled overhead, finally coming to rest on the bow of a cabin cruiser resting vertically against a belly-up mini-van.

"No chance of topping off the tank around here, I guess," he said. "Ready to press on?"

I nodded, dodging shards of a mirror underfoot. Guilt and gratitude replaced the giddiness of the adventure. *Who was I to be so selfish? Thank you, God, for giving me more than enough that I have EXTRA to put in that truck. And I*

156

don't deserve this man who would likely prefer to be in his recliner back home watching the NFL playoffs right now. Stupid clues.

Like clockwork, we arrived at the cottage just as Hank and Kelly were driving up. In the sunlight, the charm of the place was diminished by peeling paint, piles of leaves all over the porch and green algae covering most of the rails. Kelly rolled down her window and handed me a McDonald's bag. "Brought y'all lunch, thought you might be hungry." She scanned the exterior of the cottage—her opinion was all over her face.

Hank attempted a thumbs-up without dropping his super-size fries. Jilly and her baby brother were napping in their car seats.

In less than an hour, the truck was emptied and we stood waving, watching as they disappeared out of sight.

With no cable or internet yet, we quietly put things in place. Sheets on the bed, coffee in the cupboard, pots, pans, all in place after wiping things down and putting down paper towels as shelf liners. The wind was kicking up outside, causing the lights to flicker. Unable to see the humor, and seeing the possibility of no power, we locked eyes for a second, then finished the task.

"Want me to put air in your bike tires?" he asked, pulling out a hand pump from the bottom of the last box.

"That would be great, if you're not too tired. Are you hungry?"

"I sure am—if you're taking orders, I'll have a t-bone, medium rare, a loaded baked potato . . ."

I held up a red-and-white can of bean with bacon soup. "When you can have *this?*"

"Ahhh, a woman after my heart!"

The flickering continued as I maneuvered the hand can opener then reached for the box of kitchen matches on the window sill. The burner lit easily, taking no time to warm the soup to bubbling. From the other room, I could hear him shifting to fill up the last tire. I placed some crusty bread on a plate between the two mugs, butter beside the bread. "Done!" he shouted from the other room, just as the room went black. I stood there, looking at the blue flame under the soup, all spirit of adventure gone.

"Where are those kitchen matches?" he shouted.

"Right here."

"Meet you halfway." I heard him groaning to get up off the floor, then a crash as he knocked over the bicycle in the process.

"You ok?"

"Yeah, don't trip over the bike." In the dark, he took the matches from me, then struck one, lighting the candle on the little table.

"Sorry I don't have a bread knife to slice this," I whispered, tearing a hunk of bread, handing it to him and fighting back even more apologies that had nothing to do with the bread.

The next morning, he brought me coffee in bed. With no bedside table, I took the cup from him, looked at him, and said, "Thank you for your great attitude with all of this craziness."

"Well, I decided to dance." His gaze met mine directly.

158

"Excuse me?"

"That country song they were playing on that station yesterday, something like 'if you get the chance to sit it out or dance, I hope you dance'—I decided to dance."

CHAPTER TWENTY-ONE

Having returned the UHaul, Eliot tossed his backpack in the passenger seat, then turned to look at me as he started the car. "Not too late to go back with me," he said.

"I'll see you next weekend," I answered. I stood on the porch long after he had rounded the corner and was out of sight, part of me thinking maybe he'd come back and we'd talk about all of this. Risk saying what was stuck deep inside each of us, both too afraid to speak it first. For now, he was headed home. Alone. When the sky was black, I went inside.

With no cable, internet, or telephone, there was nothing to soften the sounds of night: a branch falling on the roof in the wind, a barking dog, a car slowing, then stopping, then accelerating. And the sound of waves lapping against the shore. I studied the lock on the front door and wished for a deadbolt. The back door was secured with a skeleton key and was half glass at the top. With no window coverings, I wondered who could watch me as I moved from room to room. Then a car again, slowing, stopping. I switched off all the lights and peered out. The car moved on.

I felt my way to the couch and sat there, listening. A creak on the porch caused me to duck, lying flat on the couch, waiting. *Now I understand why people own guns and attack dogs and sleep with sharp knives.* I did a mental weapon inventory. *No gun, no dog, stainless butter knife, dirty in the sink.* Sometime later, I felt my way to the bed, crawled under the covers fully dressed, and slept.

A rush of sounds, like a Naturescapes CD turned on high, flooded the place, making me want to put my hands over my ears. Realizing I was still alive, I stretched and took a deep breath. The serenade was real. Birds, church bells, more birds. I propped up and looked around. The old heart pine floors were the color of honey in rays of sunlight. A cardinal was building a nest in the azalea bush outside the window. A magnolia bud was ready to burst open just over the swing. Brown pelicans flew surveillance over the glassy water, stopping mid-air, spiraling down corkscrew-fashion to score a fish, downing it with one gulp. A pair of kayakers paddled effortlessly past, each wearing sun hats to match their crafts, one yellow and one turquoise. And I waited for coffee that didn't come.

That day and the next, I stayed inside and studied my surroundings. On the bay side, a neighbor lady tending her satsuma tree, putting the ripe ones in her apron pockets. On the street side, an occasional jogger or cyclist struggling to make it up the steep hill. Having no phone, cable, or internet, I sat cross-legged on the living room floor, plugged in the television, and hoped to tune in a local channel. Through heavy static, I caught what appeared to be a soap opera but couldn't tune in the sound. I knew I would have to get on the bike and find a place with a signal so I could get the cable and internet connected.

I hadn't ridden in a few years and finding my balance was impossible on the hills. So I walked the bicycle the few blocks toward the downtown area, stopping every few feet to see if my phone had a better signal. Six blocks later, I had three bars of cell signal. I called the studio first. The voice mail played my recorded message, "You have reached Vicki's Dance Centers..." Pushing the bike past cafes, galleries, and shops, I realized I had no idea where I was going and, on a larger scale, I had no plan. Not even a bike lock.

No plan. I had *never* been without a plan that I could recall. I would awaken each day with my calendar and my to-do list in my mind. If I were going somewhere, I'd have a map and a timeline. So here I was, pushing an increasingly heavy bicycle along the flower-lined sidewalks in a strange village without any idea where I thought I was going. I pushed the kickstand into place and sat on a bench near an outdoor café. The kickstand collapsed, landing the bike on its side across the sidewalk.

"Need some help there?" a young man offered.

"No, I'll get it, but thanks," I heard myself say. I was good at declining help and, eventually, people stopped asking.

"Bike rack over there." The young man gestured across the street.

"Thanks," I responded.

I pushed the bike into a slot, wondering if I could trust leaving it there with no chain. Then I walked away from my only mode of transportation, resigned to the fact that I couldn't lug it with me. I went back to the bench across the street and watched my bike, watched people walk past it, watched people sitting under kiwi-colored umbrellas eating, laughing, taking pictures of each other, people walking dogs. I longed for a familiar face.

I decided to go to the little inn where I'd stayed the night a few months before. The desk person said, "Hey, welcome back! Are you here for a room or a meal, or both?"

"Neither," I said flatly.

"Alright! It's good to see you again. Are you just passing through?" she inquired.

"No, I rented a little place." I pointed in a direction, then pointed in another direction, not knowing which way was home.

"Ahhhh, well, good to see you again, drop in anytime if we can be a resource for anything!" And she turned to greet a couple there for dining.

I stood there, wanting to be near the one familiar person within hundreds of miles. Then I noticed a stack of maps on the counter. "May I?" I asked the dining room server nearby.

"Sure, absolutely."

I sat on the porch swing of the inn, studying my map. It was cartoony, with drawings of the local spots. Within a few minutes, I had a plan. I'd go to the library to perhaps use a computer and then the market for a few groceries, then back to my bike and the cottage.

At the library, I scheduled cable and internet at the get-acquainted special six-month rate. Same amount of time as the lease on the cottage. Soonest they could install was ten days and no amount of begging would change that. I sent an email to Bonnie, Leslie, and Ellie, letting them know I was having difficult cell service and, hopefully, all was well, and I'd call them in a bit. I sent Eliot a quick note, along with

Kelly and Robby. I checked my incoming mail, hoping for a note from Karol, forgetting for a moment that she had removed herself, still wanting not to believe it. I got a library card and checked out two books: one about Fairhope and a second one written by Thoreau.

The little market had all I could need, but I was limited to the space of my bike basket, assuming my bike would be there waiting for me. And it was, along with a few other bikes, also untethered.

I studied the cartoon map, stuffed it in my jacket pocket, and headed home, wobbling a bit before I found my rhythm. The downhill trek reminded me of my carefree childhood days when I'd stay out after dark, riding, exploring, unafraid and wonder filled. I coasted back to the cottage, occasionally applying the brake and rarely needing to pedal.

When I walked in, the entire bay side of the cottage had a red orange glow, a sure sign that a fire was outside. There was no smoke smell, no foggy haze of a fire though. When I entered the bedroom, I stood at the windows mesmerized. The sun was setting with a show of color I'd never seen. The entire sky was consumed with brushstrokes of brilliant hues. I thought of how my schedule had me missing sunsets for most of my life. I sat on the bed beside the bag of groceries and watched the show, realizing that the peeling paint around me no longer mattered. And the fact that there were no window coverings was mattering less.

After a dinner of grapes and poached eggs, I began to hang up the few things I'd brought to wear. On the top shelf in the closet was an old rabbit ears antenna for assisting with TV reception. After an hour, I had it screwed to the back of the television, careful to keep the tin foil scrunched around the top. I adjusted the angles again and again, turning the channels, until I finally got a picture with accompanying volume on one channel. The televangelist boomed, "Let It Go, brothers and sisters!" With nothing else to fill my evening, I sat back and listened. "There are people who can walk away from you. And hear me when I tell you this! When people can walk away from you, let them walk. Your destiny is never tied to anybody that left. And you've got to know when people's part in your story is over!"

And with that, the sound turned to static. I turned off the TV and tried to absorb the message. I knew I needed to move on, but I wondered what moving on looked like. Would I smile again? Would I have friends? No to that one, for sure. If I was no longer needed at the studios on a daily basis, what would I do? I had become defined by my role and the people associated with that role. Now what?

The phone beside me vibrated, incoming call from Eliot. I answered it just as we were cut off. Then again. And again. It was clear that we couldn't connect, and he had no way to reach me. Or me him. And he likely hadn't checked email. I wasn't brave enough to walk toward town in the dark until I had a signal. After try number four, he stopped calling. I attempted to text him, repeatedly getting a fail to send message. I had never been out of touch, no matter where or what. I made sure that I was always available in case I was needed. I made a plan to go into town first thing in the morning.

The boom of thunder and flashes of lightning before dawn changed my plans. I made coffee and dropped the last slice of bread in the toaster, ready to pull the plug when the toast appeared brown. When I unplugged the toaster and the toast popped out, it flew across the tiny kitchen like a Frisbee. Not able to snag it, it hit the floor. I could hear Eliot's voice in my mind, proclaiming five-second rule, as I blew the floor dust off into the sink and took a bite.

I would be glad to see Eliot, share with him the feeling of sanctuary I had in the bay cottage, stripped of my usual comforts. I hoped he would see what a magical place this was.

CHAPTER TWENTY-TWO

"I'm heading your way Friday, should take me about five and a half hours, depending on traffic in Baton Rouge," I think Eliot said. The cell signal was sporadic a couple of blocks from the cottage, allowing choppy conversation at best. He was leaving after work and would be in late. It had been a week with little conversation between us.

"Call me when you exit I-10, ok? And even if I can't hear you, I'll know where you are."

"Will do," he said.

This would be his first weekend at the cottage since he dropped me off. The late-winter weather forecast was for brilliant sunshine, highs in the sixties. I cut some white camellias from the yard and floated them in a bowl of water on his mother's painted drop-leaf table by the window. Lacking decorations, I lined the sill with shells and sea glass I had collected from the water's edge, interspersed with white tea lights. And a cobalt blue bottle I found beside someone's trash. The old butter-colored sofa faced the bay, blending with the cream walls and the peeling white trim. A worn wicker coffee table I bought at a neighborhood yard sale held a plate of granny smith apples and the books I checked out at the library.

The etouffee was simmering, filling the tiny kitchen with smells of shrimp, green onions, bell peppers, and spicy seasonings. I'd slice the crusty bread later, after I put the rice on. Pulling the two wine glasses down from the shelf beside the sink, I stirred the steamy mixture, then went to ready my secret spot.

I had discovered it accidentally, looking for a place to put a few empty boxes and storage containers. Behind my open bedroom door was another, smaller door, stuck shut from moisture or paint. A closet, I thought, until I forced it open. I had grabbed a flashlight and shivered as the beam of light disclosed a narrow staircase. I was face to face with a major downside to being alone here. I was alone. No one to call and say, "Hey, get over here and let's see where this leads." So, I did the only logical, second-best thing: I shoved my bicycle and everything of any weight up against that door, pots and dishes that would at least make noise should something from within try to come down and visit during the night.

Then, the next day, I opened all of the windows, moved the pile of stuff, crammed my cell phone in my pocket, arming myself with a black iron skillet in one hand and flashlight in the other. I don't know where the term heebie jeebies came from, but by the time I made it to the fourth step, I had a full-blown case of them. There were seven steps to the landing, then a right-angle and more steps. I stood on the landing looking up, then BAM! The door behind me had slammed shut from the wind, me screaming a profanity as loud and long as my lungs would allow. Dropping the skillet and taking the seven stairs down in two, I pushed against the door and then pushed again, finally slamming into it with my shoulder with such velocity that I ended up sprawled across the bed. I jumped up to keep my eye on the open door.

Propping the door open with the bicycle and determined to conquer this before nightfall, and with Eliot coming soon, I had scaled the seven steps, reached the landing, retrieved the skillet and proceeded. Three steps from the top, there was nothing but an expanse of blackness. Scanning the space with the beam, I was still not clear if this was an attic or something different. I needed more light. Glancing upward, stepping backward, I backtracked, iron weapon held high. The orange outdoor extension cord running from the living room plug to the bedroom lamp caught my eye. Tossing the flashlight on the bed, I grabbed the lamp. With torch held high and armed with my frying device, I reached the top. Turning full circle, the extension cord was now loosely wrapped around my ankles. It was a small, empty, carpeted room, a door against the far wall. The orange wire had reached its max. Placing the lamp down and stepping out of the loop, I walked toward the door and forced the brass slide latch open, turned the glass doorknob, and tugged hard. The piercing light flooded the space as I blinked to focus. Before me, the bay was alive with the Friday regatta, dozens of white sails in the distance, a ballet choreographed to the music of the wind. Below, through the branches of a magnificent magnolia tree, I could see my swing. I was on a rooftop deck, an eight-foot-square vantage with a short decorative rail that reached just below my knees. I stepped gingerly, testing each step, praying I wouldn't find a soft spot that would send me crashing down onto the living room floor.

I hoped Eliot would love this magical makeshift deck as much as I did. I had set up our two folding lawn chairs out there, placing tea lights along the three sides of railing. I'd sneak up here and light the candles after dinner before leading him up the stairs. I imagined we would sit up there, taking in the beauty, both amazed at this place. Sitting in one of the chairs, I surveyed the area below. To my right, my neighbor, Patsy, was showing a little girl how to pick a satsuma from the tree beside her porch; I faintly heard her instruction to twist rather than tug until the fruit is released. Patsy applauded as the orange citrus was freed into the tiny hand. A flock of gulls squawked and dove to catch scraps of bread being thrown from the pier to my left by a young couple who later lingered, holding hands, gazing outward at the expanse of white-frosted, navy blue water. In only a few days, I had begun to fall in love with this place.

I greeted Eliot at the door, excited about our little weekend rendezvous. While eating our etouffee, he asked where the remote was, so he could watch the news. "Oh, the cable isn't working yet. Sorry, honey. They'll be here this coming Wednesday, said I don't need to be here for the cable hookup and I can pick up the modem for the internet next time I'm in town."

"Alright then, I'll watch it on your laptop; where do you have it set up?" He hadn't heard what I said and, apparently not yet understood that no cable meant no internet. I stared at him, watching and waiting for him to connect the dots. His hopeful expectancy quickly dissolved into reality. "You have *got* to be kidding me." I continued to wait, knowing this was about to escalate. "How in the hell am I gonna watch the Super Bowl? Dammit! I took off Monday so I could stay here and watch it with you!"

I shrugged, seeing the weekend fall apart. "So sorry, honey, I guess we can go to the pub downtown and watch it there maybe."

"Naw, we'll just head home early Sunday, be back in Louisiana in time for the pre-game. I can't believe you've been here for a week with no TV."

I wanted to remind him that I had never been home in the evenings, didn't have regular shows, and relied on him to keep me informed on the weather forecast. I wanted to tell him about the sunsets and riding the bike downhill and how he may enjoy it here. It wasn't the time for an argument. After dinner, I tiptoed upstairs to remove the tea lights from the rails and lock the door to the roof deck. I decided to stay for another week and be there for the cable folks rather than head back with him.

"Hey!" I heard him shouting. "Where's the bathroom door?"

"Oh, the pocket door got stuck inside the wall. I called the landlord about it. She said it can't be fixed, that's why I have that sheer curtain there as our door."

"Really? What if, what if I have to . . .?"

I had rounded the corner and saw him standing there exhausted and powerless, staring at the sheer door. "What if you have to take a *private moment*?"

"Yes," he sighed. "How will people know not to waltz in here?"

I wanted to point out the obvious, that there would be no people any time soon, since we knew absolutely no one here. Instead, I got creative and offered a suggestion. "How about if you find a tune you've downloaded on your cell phone and play it as your signal to be left alone?"

"I'm too tired to have this conversation," he said.

The next morning after breakfast, I heard the opera *Un Belle Di* coming from the direction of the bathroom.

When I suggested I stay for the cable installation rather than going back with him, there was no resistance. He took a container of etouffee and put it in the little cooler he kept in his car. We agreed that he would come back in two weeks and we'd go back home together. Recital season was approaching and, although I would accomplish a lot on email and phone, I was accustomed to helping sort costumes, answer the studio phone during the day, set up dance portraits, prepare the program book, plan for the ticketing process, monitor class progress, order awards, and make myself available.

Although he didn't turn toward me as he pulled out of the driveway, I waved goodbye until he turned up the hill onto Fairhope Avenue and out of sight.

CHAPTER TWENTY-THREE

I was learning that the pace in Fairhope was very different from home. No one appeared to be in a rush, including the cable and internet guy who arrived four hours after the appointed time. "I tried to call you on the number you gave us," he apologized.

"That's my cell number, doesn't work here," I replied.

"You reset it to pick up the tower here?" he asked.

"No, how do I do that?" I sighed impatiently.

"Here, I'll do it for you if you like," he offered, reaching out his hand.

He fiddled with my phone for a few minutes, then said, "There, that should help some. Won't be great reception here on the water, but you should be able to get a signal most often, especially if you go outside. Now, where's your TV?"

I gestured to the set on the living room floor, foil-wrapped antennae adorning the top.

"Wow, ok then." He began to whistle a tune as he manipulated wires, then asked where my computer was so he could check the internet.

It became clear why this guy was late. He had an easy breezy attitude that appeared to carry no stress. He was doing his job as best he could, lending a hand where needed, knowing he'd get it all done in due time. I felt embarrassed

173

by my assumption that this young man was arrogant and didn't respect my time. I took a deep breath and felt gratitude surface. I'd be back in touch with my world and able to be reached, finally. That's what mattered.

The two weeks passed quickly. I'd gotten caught up with studio work, talked daily with Bonnie, Leslie, and Ellie when I went toward town. I was able to receive texts, but reception for phone conversations was inconsistent at best. I found a cardboard box, covered it with a towel and turned it into a TV stand for when Eliot would come. I had found some faded window sheers at a yard sale and hung them on the rods in the bedroom and living room. Although they didn't block the view, they lent a softness to the space and mirrored how I felt there, softer. My few clothes were kept folded on the shelf in the closet and the laundromat downtown was within easy distance for biking. I was getting better at peddling uphill and I wondered if I'd ever be there with my car.

Since Eliot was at work during the day, it would be after dark before we could talk by phone. So, we didn't talk much during that time. When I did venture outside at night, I was amazed at how the sidewalk traffic was pretty much the same as during the day: people walking dogs, jogging, bicycling. Most alone, illuminated by the street lights along the bay front.

When Eliot returned, he was full of chatter about his work, the weeds popping up in the yard, Izzy, and the stack of mail I needed to go through. We sat out on the swing by the bay and, after a long silence, he said, "You know, this just isn't practical."

I tried to digest what was unspoken but couldn't. "What isn't practical, Eliot?"

"This place here," he said slowly.

We both gazed outward across the water, not swinging, just still. The triple-masted schooner, Joshua, was sailing out in the distance, gulls and pelicans perched on pilings nearby waiting for a ripple in the water.

Eliot continued, "I mean, people don't *do* this. They work every day, they come home. They go to the movies or dinner on the weekends. That's what people do. This just isn't practical, honey."

A kayaker in the distance fought to reel in a nice-sized fish.

I didn't want to be the opposing party to an argument that could not be won. "Eliot, don't you have any *somedays*?" I asked softly. "You know, those things you say to yourself: *someday* I'd like to . . .?"

"Of course I do." He sounded exasperated. "*Someday*, I'd like to do that." He pointed to the kayak fisherman, out there all alone, baiting his hook.

"Eliot, can't we have just a little bit of *someday* now?" I turned to face him. "We have a six-month lease here; can't we get out of our norm a bit?"

"The guys at work are asking if you're having an affair." He turned away from me. "And I said I didn't think so. They don't understand this." He gestured to the cottage.

There it was, the guys at work. "I would bet most of those guys have hunting or fishing camps. That's what they do in Louisiana, right?"

"Yes, but what's your point?" he asked.

175

"My point is that they don't understand this because they have no frame of reference. Tell them we've rented a camp in Alabama and we spend time there. That should clear up their questions," I said confidently.

"So, what you're saying is that . . ." His question trailed off.

"What I'm saying is that maybe our *someday* is now. Why do we push those wishes off into the distant future when, just maybe, we can begin to live some of them now?" It was the first real conversation we had had in a very long time. No TV, no Izzy, no familiar. Just us, on a rusty swing, in a different setting, perhaps defining our new norm.

That afternoon, we rented a two-person kayak. The bay was choppy and we pushed away from the shore against a stiff wind, having no clue how to paddle or steer. It had looked easy from the swing. The wind pushed us out a bit and we each began to paddle. And we went around and around in a circle, making no forward progress.

"Hey!" a guy throwing a cast net from a nearby pier shouted. "As long as you are paddling in opposite directions, you'll never get anywhere!"

CHAPTER TWENTY-FOUR

Back at the studio, things were buzzing. The new competition teams had grown, as new transfers requested special auditions. Classes were full and the new staff was all on task. The atmosphere was upbeat and, for the most part, drama-free. We had an opportunity to redefine our mission statement: we would be the clean and classy ones, not stooping to the seductive moves and music so popular today. We would be about excellence in technique, making sure to encourage each child's unique gifts and talents. We would be against the norm when defining stereotypical dancers.

The studio had become a business where people respected one another. And I began to realize how, before, much chaos and energy had been going into massaging some insatiable egos. I wondered if we could be successful when we were unwilling to sell out to the trends, instead, holding fast to the goal of producing fine, confident dancers. I had paid a price, as had my family, sacrificing much to keep the staff happy. I wondered if I would ever be free of the regret of the years invested.

A week before recital, I ordered flowers for the staff and for myself, my favorite flowers in my favorite colors. The illusions were gone, as were the expectations.

Bonnie, Leslie, Ellie, and I gathered before the show, each of us quietly honoring the others, having walked through a season that none of the parents or dancers would ever understand.

With summer classes at capacity and all rolling smoothly, I made a plan to drive to the cottage and spend some extended time there. As I crossed the bay, I opened the windows and welcomed the sea air—pelicans, gulls, shrimp boats all seemed to wrap me in a feeling of sanctuary, a safe retreat from a community that continued to have awkward encounters at every turn. I wept as though I was falling into the arms of a lover. Mostly, I felt that I was home.

Strangely, sleeping in this place on the Eastern Shore of Mobile Bay had been fairly easy. Despite being alone and having only sheers on the windows, I felt like a child after a long day of playing outside, ready to curl up, feeling protected. I'd become accustomed to opening the few windows with screens on mild nights, drifting off to the sound of the incoming tide.

One night, shouting and the sound of running across the ground outside jolted me upright. Through the sheers, lights slashed in every direction, then toward my bedroom. My thoughts came in rapid-fire questions: *Was this a home invasion? What did I have to protect myself? Where could I hide? Should I run? Where would I go?* I ducked as the lights once again pointed toward my windows. "Woooooo Hooooooo!" The threatening voices got louder. Desperately wanting to scream or cry for help, I realized no one would hear me except the invaders. Their numbers could be in the hundreds, maybe a gang of renegades preying on this quiet area where people slept with their windows open. I had never asked anyone if this place was safe.

Easing out of bed and crouching below the window sill, I grabbed my jacket and pulled it on over my pajamas, careful not to be seen. I made a plan. I'd crawl toward the back door, grabbing my keys, staying low, and make my way out to my car. *What if they had a lookout posted there? God, why have I watched so many TV crime shows? Why didn't I leave the windows closed? Those screens are so flimsy.* I was groping on the counter for the keys, careful to keep low, only my hand searching the formica above my head.

The crowd was now directly outside, suddenly erupting in laughter, female voices among them. And then, *was that splashing? This was anything but funny. Was this some sort of practical joke, teenagers bored and maybe wanting to scare the daylights out of people in the middle of the night? Or was this an initiation rite, like hazing, for new residents of this strange little place?*

Curiosity drew me on all fours back toward the windows, where I peered out, just my eyes above the sill. I blinked, testing to see if I was hallucinating, seriously doubting I was seeing this accurately. There was my band of terrorists: women, men, and children, maybe twenty of them in the dark, at the water's edge, flashlights and buckets and *spears?* Then a brief spotlight on a blonde toddler wearing a yellow Beauty and the Beast nightgown.

Clearly, I was witnessing a cult ritual of some sort and they even had kids connected. Waves of fear rushed back as I wondered if there would be some sort of sacrifice involved and if I was part of their plan. Among the group, I spotted a familiar figure, Patsy, my neighbor. *She had seemed so normal as she welcomed me with tomatoes from her garden.* I wondered if there was an effort to seduce me into something so pagan that gatherings are only in the middle of the night? I sat and listened.

I must have drifted off sometime after the crowd dispersed, sitting against the wall near the window, jacket on, keys nearby. It was daylight. I stood and surveyed the area outside the window for any sign of what I had witnessed. Nothing. A fisherman heading out against the soft gray pre-dawn sky, the occasional squawking of a giant blue heron, no validation of my traumatic night anywhere. I walked the interior of the cottage, examining windows and doors for any sign of attempted entry. If anyone had wanted to get in, they would have had no problem. Illusions of being safe were gone.

Realizing I could have disappeared last night leaving no evidence of my whereabouts, I had to tell someone. *Eliot? No, he already thought this was too crazy and would insist I leave immediately, never to return. Not a bad idea, actually.* I grabbed my cell phone and headed out to sit in my car, hoping for a cell signal there. I'd call my daughter, Kelly, at seven, wait in a secure place till then.

Trying to run across crushed shell in pink fuzzy slippers was tricky. I had one hand on the car door. "Good morning!" Patsy had spotted me as she stooped to pick up the *Mobile Press Register*. I raised my arm in greeting, careful not to make eye contact, rushing to slam the door behind me and lock it. *Close call.*

VICKI ARMITAGE

Right at seven, Kelly answered on the first ring. "Mom? What's *wrong*? Are you ok?"

"Morning, Kel, how are y'all?" I tried to sound casual and chatty.

"Mom, in case you've forgotten, this is Kelly, your daughter. You *never* call me at the crap of dawn. Are you sick?"

The more I thought about my night, the crazier it sounded. "No, I'm *fine*! Just called to tell you about something a little strange that happened."

"I *knew* it! Something *has* happened. Hank! Check on the kids, will you, something's happened to Mom."

"Wait, Kel."

"Mom, tell me exactly where you are this minute."

"Well, *actually,* I'm sitting in the car outside the cottage. "

"Mom, you are never out this early. Hank! See if you can take the day off, I need to go down and see about Mom." She was ready to rescue me, not needing any details. I wondered if I was that transparent. "Ok, Mom, it's almost seven-fifteen right now. I can be there about ten."

"Kel, go tell Hank to go on to work. I'm just up early; thought I'd tell you a little about my neighbors. Didn't mean to scare you; call me back after breakfast."

"Mom, should I be worried about you?"

"No indeed—I'm just fine. Y'all have a good day and we'll chat later." I heard one of the children calling her, so it was the perfect time to cut it short. I waited to see if she bought it. "Ok, but I *will* call you back in a bit." A temporary respite from her interrogation and, somehow, I felt comforted she was alerted.

I argued with myself about calling the Fairhope Police, then wondered who may be allied with this group, some of them could be Fairhope's finest, sworn to protect and defend.

From inside my litter-strewn SUV, I watched the sidewalk come alive with early morning joggers, dog-walkers, and trash collectors. The trash truck's automated arm scooped up my green wheeled container, tossing the contents into its growling belly, setting it down with a thud. Scared a weenie dog walking its elderly owner, both almost colliding with a cyclist pedaling hard to make it up the steep hill. I felt comforted, seeing all of these strangers nearby. Cautiously, I unlocked the car door and edged toward the cottage.

"*There* you are!" It was Patsy, a few feet away, proudly holding a zip-loc bag extended in my direction.

"Uh, hi." It was as though she hadn't noticed I was wearing my pajamas.

"Crab cakes. Made 'em fresh this morning. Thought you'd like some with your breakfast. Hard to beat fresh crab cakes with your eggs."

I reached for the bag. "Thanks."

Rather than invite her in, I walked with her around to the side of the cottage, toward the bay, hoping to guide her back home.

"Did you sleep through the commotion last night?"

There it was. "Commotion?" I assumed this was a hook of some sort and I didn't take it. "What do you *mean*?"

"Honey, we had us a *jue-bill-eee*. I'm surprised you didn't hear all the whoopin' and hollerin'."

"A *what?*" I couldn't help it, I had to hear the explanation she'd give me.

"A *jubilee!*" It must have been abundantly clear from my blank expression that I didn't speak the code language. Honey, you don't know what a jubilee is?"

I bit my lip, shaking my head slowly, studying her. Her soft gray hair and weathered face framed kind, blue-gray eyes. For a second, my guard had slipped.

"Oh my heavens, girl, let's sit here on the swing." She patted the cedar seat as she steadied the chain with her right hand.

I was too tired to conjure up an exit, and the swing, at the edge of the water out in the wide-open daylight, seemed ok. "Looka, there's Ichabod. Out there waiting for him a snack."

"Ichabod?" I wondered if she was pointing to some imaginary character only she could see.

"Crane! Ichabod Crane! See him out there?"

"You mean that big bird?" I only saw a great blue heron on a pier piling, standing still as a sculpture. The wake from a passing shrimp boat splashed against a beach ball left too close, tugging it out under the pier. A fishy breeze folded Patsy's pink-and-yellow-flowered bibbed apron over on itself. She smoothed it back down, chuckling as though she had been tickled.

"Yes! *That's my friend, Ichabod!*" He shows up every morning, about this time.

As we looked out toward the big pier to our right, Patsy spun a tale about how, when weather and timing converge, there are only two places in the world where this event happens. "Between June and September, usually in the middle of the night, the oxygen in the water gets low and all of the shrimp and fish and crabs come right up here on the shore, thousands of 'em, just for us to scoop up and fill our freezers." She punctuated her last three words by tapping on the bag in my lap. She couldn't have been more confusing. Or maybe I needed coffee.

"Looka here." She stood and pointed down in the water. "See 'em?"

I stood slowly, trying to allow this bizarre tale to mesh with my night's experience.

"They're smoking."

"Smoking?"

"Yes, look, the mullets—all trying to get some oxygen." Sure enough, a few fish had their mouths, er *snouts*, ahhh *faces* puckered up and out of the water. Their smacking sound was a cross between raindrops and popcorn popping. "Come on, there may be shrimp down there too." She grabbed my sleeve, tugging me down to where she was pulling a wadded net out of a white plastic five-gallon bucket, the word LARD painted red on the side, the rest too worn to make out. She handed me a wet pile as she unfurled another. I watched her put a metal weight tied to the edge in her mouth as she pleated the folds of the bundle with both hands. The motion reminded me of my grandma dealing canasta, those hands moving so fast. Somehow, Patsy wrapped a rope around her wrist and spun the thing out over the water where it splashed in a perfect circle then disappeared down below the surface. She pulled the rope, hand over hand, the mesh rising up with the bottom all closed, a silvery foot-long fish and some shrimp inside. Holding the web over the bucket, she somehow released the catch then turned back to the bay for more.

"Take off that jacket, girl, we've got dinner to catch."

The rest of the morning, I studied the art of throwing a cast net from the master, my neighbor. Most often, mine splash-landed in a shape resembling a triangle or a crescent moon. But, twice, the coveted perfect circle. For me, having that circle hit that water was more satisfying than the catch, although I did score a baby jellyfish and two shrimp. "Looka," she'd say. "Those are flounder down there on the bottom, the things that look like magnolia leaves under there." I released my catch into the bucket, learning how to unlatch the gizmo on the grid causing it to open up at the bottom, watching Patsy zero in on the magnolia leaf flounder.

She pointed to the sun. "Well, I think we've done a morning's worth." I stood there soaked in bay water wearing the Hello Kitty pajamas Kelly had given me for Christmas. As if on cue, my jacket pocket muffled "*I Heard it Through the Grapevine.*"

"Hi, Kel."

"Whatcha doin', Mom?"

"Ahhhh, not much, you?"

Later, I stood under a warm shower in my pjs, allowing the bay water and thoughts of crazed gangs to wash away. I knew that if Kelly and Eliot had talked, an intervention could be in the works. Through my makeshift bathroom door, a faded window sheer, I could see a cruise ship heading to port in Mobile, its red and blue smokestack shaped like a cartoon whale's tail. I had placed the phone on the edge of the sink, knowing everything else needed to be rinsed. My slippers, no longer pink, squished sand through my toes. As I stripped down, squirting shampoo on the wet clothes, the phone began to vibrate on the porcelain surface. I reached for it, seeing the caller ID beginning to fog, Eliot. I pressed the talk button, shutting off the shower with the other hand.

"Hey there."

"Hey yourself. You sound a little muffled, whatcha doing?"

I sized up the pile of sheets and dirty laundry on the floor, trying to plan my trek to the laundromat. Although I rarely used it, I was glad to have my car handy. The laundromat was unlike those from any point of reference in my past. This little place served coffee and muffins in the morning and wine and cheese in the evenings. The atmosphere was social and welcoming. I still missed the convenience of having in-house machines. Back home, I opened the doors and windows, allowing the salty air to flow through the cottage. Folded neatly on my top step and secured with a bag of sweet potatoes, the Saturday paper was left for me by an unknown benefactor. Patsy, maybe? The classifieds seemed a diversion from putting sheets on the bed, so I spread the papers out on the bed and turned to the "Appliance" category. I scanned the listing, finding prices that far exceeded my non-existent budget for a temporary home.

"What are you doing indoors on this glorious day?" Rita was standing in the doorway. She had walked over to introduce herself one day, saying she lived nearby. I didn't know her well, but she seemed to be the sort of person who made herself at home anywhere.

"Laundry to do, so I'm fantasizing about washers and dryers, Rita."

"You want a washer and dryer, honey? Have hookups?"

"As sparse as this place is, yes, there are hookups on the little side screened porch, just off the bedroom here."

She crossed the room to confirm, stepping out onto the side porch. "Ok, then, I'll see if Bobby can get 'em over here in a bit."

"Get what over here in a bit, Rita? And who's Bobby?"

"Your washer and dryer. I was out walking before I stopped here. There's an elderly couple moving out a couple of blocks away and they just realized they don't have room for the washer and dryer in the moving truck they rented. They're just gonna leave them, even asked if I wanted them."

"Are you saying *free,* Rita?"

"Yes I am, sister." She was out the door. "Stay here, I'll get Bobby here with his cousin's pickup."

Within an hour, a pony-tailed lanky man was at my door shouting "You Rita's friend?"

"Do you have a washer and dryer?"

"Yes, ma'am I do. Where's it gonna go?"

I walked the stranger through the bedroom and showed him the porch.

"Ah, good, you have a door to the yard out here; looks like I have enough room to pull the truck right up. Oh, by the way, I'm Bobby Lee."

He strode past me and within minutes a rusting and banged up black Ford truck was backing toward my laundry porch, shiny washer and dryer in the back.

From the bedroom door, I watched him slide the washer across the tailgate onto the porch floor and toward the spot where pipes protruded from the wall.

"Where's your cut-off valve?" he asked

"Not a clue."

Reaching through the spot where the back window of the truck once was, he pulled out a wrench and walked toward the street side of the cottage. Within minutes he shouted, "Found it!"

"Hey, try the water now." He appeared behind me, having entered through the bayfront door.

"You startled me." I turned to face him as he walked into the bedroom.

"Try the water now. Where's the closest faucet?"

"Right here, in the bathroom." I pulled back the old window sheer makeshift door and turned on the sink faucet.

"No water, Bobby Lee."

"Heeeeeyyyy, nice door. Makes for great silhouettes behind that sheer, I'll bet."

"What are you talking about?"

"Oh, just thinkin' about how a person would look undressed in there from out here. Whoa, ma'am, I didn't mean to scare you."

I was backing toward the door, stopping just short of tumbling down the steps into the yard.

"Sorry, ma'am. You don't need to be scared of me; I just love the human body, think it's the most beautiful thing God created." He turned and walked out on the porch and soon sounds of metal on metal allowed me to relax a bit as I cautiously moved to observe his work.

"Yeah, long as my family goes back, we've been naturists." He glanced up at me, then back at the pipe he held firmly with the wrench. "We just prefer not having clothes on. In fact, some of the people I work for let me . . ."

"Not me, Bobby Lee. I prefer my washer dryer installers fully clothed." I tried to sound more comfortable than I was.

He continued to work. And talk. "Yeah, ain't nothing feels better than sage grass under your feet and long-leaf pine saplings against your skin."

I had to ask. "So, your whole family are nudists?"

"Oh, yes, ma'am. Way back, much of Fairhope was. Three nudist colonies were here. People would just walk out of their houses and down to the bay to bathe."

"You mean they would just strip down, right there on the beach?"

"Oh, no, ma'am. They'd just walk out their door, through their neighborhood and stroll down to the water in all their beauty. Except one very large lady up on Summit Street. She apparently wore her bathrobe, but let it flap open in the breeze. I sure could use a soft drink." He wiped his forehead with the back of his hand.

Not wanting to turn my back on him, I walked backward toward the kitchen and pulled a root beer out of the fridge.

"Thanks. Yes'm, I sure do wish it was still that way here. Only time I've ever been arrested was for what they called indecent—me laid out in the sun right down there on Magnolia Beach. People would come from all over to be in the natural. Some of the wealthier folks here even built cabins on their property for out-of-town visitors."

"Now, let's see if we're in business here." He walked toward me and I backed out of his way as he went outside.

"Ok, try that water now."

Obediently, I backed into the bathroom. "We have water, Bobby Lee."

"Alrighty, let's see if this here washer is gonna fill up." He turned the washer dial and, after a good deal of sputtering, I could hear water flowing.

"Well, damn. Got the hot and cold reversed. Guess I'll have to start over."

"Oh, no. It'll be just fine like that. No need to start over."

"Whatever you say." He pushed the washer into place and turned to retrieve the dryer.

"So, Bobby Lee, we're not just talking only a few people who used to do this?"

He laughed. "No, indeed, it was a lot of what they now call ultra-liberal people here. All having a grand time out on the beach, down by the bay."

"You mean like gatherings?"

"Oh, yes. And the kids whose families didn't participate would sneak up to the bluff and lay on their bellies watching it all below. It's not sexual or anything like that. You get that, right?"

I nodded yes, but truly did not get that.

"So, based on your chosen lifestyle, I'm assuming there are still others around here who ummm *practice* this?"

"Oh, yes, ma'am. In fact, some of the people I work for, doing odd jobs, are practicing naturists. Hey, there's some laundry soap in this here cabinet!"

I watched him examine the two-twenty plug for the dryer. "So, are there still gatherings?"

"Ah, yes, mostly over in Milton, though. A fella bought a bunch of land and planted all the right stuff, so we mostly have to go over there." He turned the dial on the dryer and punched start. The drum began to tumble. "Want to put something in there? Seems to be heating up just fine."

"No, Bobby Lee, thanks anyway. How much do I owe you? I sure do appreciate you doing this."

"The root beer's good enough pay, ma'am. Let Rita know if you need anything else. I'll be glad to help you." He stuck his head in to look at the bathroom curtain door. "Ummmm ummm, sure do like that."

I latched the screen door as he got in the truck, then went and closed the other doors. As I gathered up the sheets to put in the wash, I wondered how Rita knew Bobby Lee and how much of Fairhope's past still existed around me.

CHAPTER TWENTY-FIVE

I sat in the sand, picked up a stick, and drew a figure-eight. The give and take symbol formed seamlessly through the shells and tiny rocks. I traced it again, this time carving deeper, the fluid circular motions becoming more connected each time. I watched as a wave eroded one side of the symbol, leaving frothy residue and an aqua piece of sea glass. Picking up the shard, I wiped it on my pants then tucked it in my pocket. Another wave completely erased half of my carving, leaving only one circle. *Works for me,* I decided. Sometimes being alone is easier. *Friend* had become my new f-word. I'd lost the ability to discern what it meant, I suppose. Or, I missed Friendship 101 where maybe I would have learned about reciprocity.

Climbing the stairs, I reached the landing for the boardwalk to the little Orange Street Pier, a wooden finger reaching out to the bay, a small, covered pavilion at the end, benches on either side. It was the perfect spot for ending my day, seeing the giant orange sun disappear into the sapphire water each evening. Occasionally, I'd be joined by tourists with cameras or maybe a fisherman hoping to bring home supper. Today, solitude. A crisp breeze kicked at the water, sending my hands diving into pockets for warmth. *Ouch!* I pulled out the glass, realizing that a sharp edge must have pricked my index finger. The piece was about an inch long, both ends softly rounded and brushed into a dull patina. Nothing evident to cause my bleeding finger. Underneath, a shiny jagged glass thorn, deep inside. I wondered what this once was, a bottle or vase maybe—something beautiful before a storm sent it spiraling into the depths, smashing it to worthless chunks. Over time, maybe more storms began a refining process, rocks and sand smoothing it to become someone's collected treasure or piece of jewelry.

Footsteps on the raised walkway vibrated the platform, an elderly woman in lavender sweats, sneakers, carrying a yellow duffle bag. The sun was about thirty minutes from meeting the horizon. I wondered if I really wanted to stay now that I had company.

"Hello there." She sat on one of the benches, releasing a little sigh.

"Hi," I volunteered.

Silently, we both watched the fiery show begin, only the sound of an occasional mullet splashing, likely trying to avoid being swallowed by something bigger beneath the surface.

"You know, some people say this here place is a vortex."

"Really?" She had my attention.

"Yes, indeed."

I waited for more details, watching her gazing westward.

"What do *you* think?" I prodded.

"*I* think there are lots of places around here that have special energy and this is definitely one of them."

"Where else?"

"Oh, the pitcher plant bog down near Week's Bay is one." She began to untie her shoes and peel off her socks. Standing, she pulled off the sweatshirt then her pants, revealing a rounded wrinkly body in a purple swimsuit. "You know, some people are drawn here, as if magnetically, by an unseen force and finally the longing to come back and be here permanently takes over. "Toodleoo, dear!"

Speechless, I gawked as she stepped onto the rungs of the wooden ladder, lowering herself into the waist-deep, dark water below. She began to walk toward the setting sun, now gigantic with the tiny silhouette of a curly-haired woman at its edge.

I looked around, wondering if anyone else was witness to this. Not a soul. When she reached chest-deep, she began a smooth crawl toward the horizon. Brushstrokes of purples, blues, and pinks heralded dusk as the sun slipped below the surface about the time she reached the channel marker and headed back.

It was pitch dark when she silently stepped back onto the platform, unzipped her bag, pulled out a towel, and patted dry. Grabbing her bag and shoes, she nodded toward me then walked away. Honoring the almost sacred silence, I watched her disappear into the night, wanting to shout, "Wait! Explain this! Tell me about something. Anything!" But she was gone.

On my way back to the cottage, I passed the bronze statue of an almost life-size Marietta Johnson, two of her bronze students at her feet. Seems Ms. Johnson pioneered the School of Organic Education here, believing students are taught best in and through nature and unconventional experiences. Someone had placed a pink azalea blossom in her upturned palm, spotlighted now by the full moon. I would later learn about the large live oak tree outside the classroom, where students would each claim a spot on a limb and listen to the teacher below on a picnic blanket. They would explore the gullies and learn about the plant life beneath their bare feet. They'd study tracks, they'd learn folk dancing on the beach by the bay. From this school, came dozens of creatives—writers, artists, and more.

I was awake most of the night, replaying the encounter with the woman on the pier, grasping for an understanding of her odd reference, deciding to set out and find the pitcher plant bog the next morning. At dawn, I crossed the bridge over Fish River, taking the unmarked road to the left. A round brown sign with cream lettering indicated I should park in a shallow open space in a grove of tupelo trees. It was a tourist area, yet I was the only visitor that day, no other cars around. I parked, tucked my purse under the seat, and stepped out. A rustic raised wooden walkway had a sign at its base indicating visitors should be aware of cottonmouths, a photo accompanying the warning—a striking snake. I looked down at my polka-dot flip flops and the ground around me, then leapt to the stairway leading to the boarded path and into the bog. A sharp, ninety-degree angle turn to the right seemed to head down toward the river and out of view to passersby. I considered turning back, calling it done, having seen a photo of a pitcher plant directly beside the mug of the poisonous reptile. Deciding on a peek, I edged toward the bend to see what I would miss. Swampy meadows of soft color, chirping insects, and the musky scent of stagnant water drew me closer for a better view. Before me, emerging from the bracken, thousands of stripe-throated, bud-vase-shaped blooms, each with a lip to guide rainwater toward its innards. Yellow, green, pink, purple, and coral speckles surrounded the inside of each mouth to attract its prey: the insect du jour. Some were folded tight at the top, the spout sealing it over like a present neatly wrapped. I imagined some unsuspecting critter drawn to the beauty and a spot to rest and becoming the entrée. Staring intently, I hoped to see or hear the capture, finally realizing nature is much more subtle in its seduction. I thought about organic education and realized that I had enrolled and was fully immersed as an enthusiastic student.

A rumble of thunder was my signal to turn back, despite unanswered questions about the magical powers here. Black clouds had gathered low to the south and west, chasing me back to the cottage. My grandmother, always terrified of storms, had taught me to hunker down in an interior room or bathtub when weather threatened, a bottle of aspirin nearby in case she had a heart attack, flashlight handy, ready for the house to be lifted up like in the *Wizard of Oz*. I turned on the car radio, just as the severe weather bulletin was being announced for Baldwin County: damaging winds, take cover. I accelerated to get ahead of it, remembering I had left all of the windows wide open. Barely inside, I heard children screaming out by the bay. "What the...?" I heard myself ask. There they were, maybe five children, their parents and grandparents, all lined up out on the pier next door, arms outstretched like pelicans ready for the next thermal to lift them to the heavens. Shrieking laughter, they faced the

196

approaching storm as the driving rain began, then raced each other back to their porch next door, breathless and exhilarated. I stood in my open doorway holding on to the frame as I was buffeted, watching the swells growing and crashing over the piers, feeling the stinging sideways rain, mesmerized.

The storm had barely ended when the children emerged barefoot, running back out on the wet pier with no railings, high above the water, the youngest barely a toddler. I waited for a parent to shout, "Don't run! Be careful!" or even, "Hold your brother's hand." Apparently, this scene had been played out for generations in this place.

The streets dried quickly as the sun returned, so I decided to walk to the market downtown. Passing Mr. Gene's Beans ice cream shop with its deck outside, I was drawn to a group of four women sitting at the round, wrought-iron table, giggling like teenagers, licking cones. A painter stood outside the Lyon's Share gallery next door, slashing bursts of turquoise acrylic on his canvas with a palette knife, a sleeping golden retriever at the foot of his easel. Ahead, a young girl was taping a flyer to the bookstore window. Something about a pajama party in the streets of downtown Fairhope with dancing, food, and fun. I stared at the primary-colored lettering on the paper, then looked through the glass into the bookstore coffee shop, Latté Da, beyond. Two women, deep in conversation, sat at one of the bistro tables inside, steaming mugs untouched, leaning in, expressions concerned, as though sharing a secret or weighty burden. Trying not to stare, I fiddled with my empty, canvas grocery sack, struggling to push back the flood of loneliness, missing

Karol, reminding myself of the past several months and the risks of opening my heart to others.

I opened the heavy glass door, passed the two women, and headed toward the counter laden with fresh-baked cakes and muffins. The room was filled with rich aromas and chatter, the chalk board overhead listing dozens of choices, some named after colorful locals who frequented the place. I decided on a "Fannie Jo," described as sweet and spicy like its namesake. Chicory coffee, dark chocolate, raspberry, and a slap of chili powder. Patrons in Page and Palette, the bookstore to my left, studied the staff favorites just posted.

The two women stood and, after a warm embrace, greeted a group near the door and left. I grabbed my drink and sat down at their vacated table, picked up a folded paper napkin left behind and looked around for the trash. Not wanting to lose my seat, I placed it near the edge of the table at the same time the door opened, a breeze blowing the napkin to the floor. Reaching down, I noticed the writing, in blue ink, and spread it out on the table. A list of three words with bullet points read:

- Release
- Trust
- Live!

I turned it over, smoothing out the wrinkles, trying to make out the counsel shared on the coffee-stained piece. "*Dance Naked!*"

The blonde girl behind the counter shouted, "Tickets are here for the pajama party! Anybody want to buy theirs today?" Almost involuntarily, I raised my hand.

The downtown market was easy—a few basics, and I was on my way back to the cottage, passing the places that once housed families who ferried across the bay for the summer. My shortcut through the hilly Fruit and Nut district, bordered by little Magnolia Beach, had become a haven for reclusive artists and writers, the coveted little cottages being restored with love by those seeking sanctuary surrounded by beauty and a pace that encouraged lingering over glasses of sweet tea.

The phone rang as I stepped up onto the porch. "Hey, Eliot." I plopped the bag down and sat in the old cane rocker, kicking my shoes off, putting my feet up on the rail.

His tone was icy. "So, I see you decided to cut down the tree."

I put my feet down, sitting up straight. "*Excuse* me? What did you say?"

"I *said*, I *see* you decided to cut down the tree!"

"Eliot, *what* are you talking about?"

"The *tree*, the gazillion-year-old tree, in our front yard for God's sake. The tree people are grinding the stump. Thanks a lot for including me in *that* decision!"

Click, phone dead. I looked at the screen. *Was he kidding? Did he really just hang up on me?* I dialed Susie, our next door neighbor.

"Susie, is there anything going on in our front yard?"

"Well, just the people taking down that grand live oak of yours."

I felt something welling up in my throat and could barely speak. "Susie, what did you say?"

"Your tree people are almost done, been watching them from my kitchen window all day. Breaks my heart, watching her go, she was so magnificent. I told Vincent you must have found disease or something."

"But I didn't, she wasn't, how could anyone?"

"Honey, are you saying you didn't *hire* them to come do this?"

Choking back something boiling up from deep inside, wanting to scream that something else was being ripped away from me, the words barely came out. "No, several months ago, I had three companies come out to check her out and give me a price on pruning her. I made no decisions, haven't talked with any of the contractors since."

Susie's voice was hushed and soothing. "Oh baby, and you're not here and they didn't call or anything to confirm all of this?"

"Right." I tried to swallow hard, hoping to push this away and regain composure.

"Now, you listen here. *Nothing* this bizarre happens without some divine hand protecting you from something you couldn't see. You have to try to believe that."

My chest was heaving as I hung up and ran inside to the bathroom, thinking I was about to be sick. "How *could* they?" I wailed as my knees gave way, betrayal and injustice pouring out in sobs, my cheek pressed against the cool, heart pine floor. "Why?" I heard myself cry to a God who seemed to have abandoned me.

It was dusk when I stood and walked toward the porch, picked up the phone, and called Eliot. He answered but couldn't hear me. I walked out on the pier, all the way to the end, and tried again.

"I've been trying to call you back since we got cut off," he blurted.

"I, I just can't believe it," I said.

"Susie just walked over here and told me you had no idea about this. How could someone just decide to come over and take out our tree?"

I had no response; all my energy was left on the floor back at the cottage.

"I'm just so pissed! We need to sue those bastards."

"Won't bring the tree back," I whispered.

After we each said goodbye, I laid back on the rough boards of the pier and looked up at the sky, breathing in the washed air, thinking of the past few months and trying to shift my Pollyanna thinking. I thought of the random wisdom offered me by well-wishers and strangers lately:

"Stuff happens."

"When God lifts His grace over something, it's obvious."

"People operate in their own best interest."

"Don't trust no one."

And the most unique, overheard in Julwyn's downtown diner while eating pecan pancakes, "Now whatever made you think that kindness begets kindness? Nowhere in the Bible, with all those begats, does it say that if you do people right, they's gonna do *you* right?"

I sat up and looked out across the water. The city of Mobile glittered along the shore like a diamond necklace. I thought of the people who crossed the bay in those earlier times, wondering if they, too, were grateful for the distance behind them.

Back at the cottage, I picked up the grocery sack from the porch and took it in to the kitchen. I turned on the counter lamp and pulled out the apples, the fresh-baked bread, goat cheese, and obscure wisdom on a crumpled paper napkin.

"What does one wear to a downtown pajama party on a crisp October evening?" I asked myself aloud, pulling my two pairs of PJs off the closet shelf that served as my dresser. "The Hello Kitty or the black-and-white crossword puzzle?" Examining the puzzle ones, I read the words in the blocks: calm, peace, serene. Maybe the words would be a camouflage for the discomfort in my gut.

I was close enough to walk but driving seemed smarter. I imagined a clip on page four in the *Fairhope Courier*: "Woman found wandering Fruit and Nut District in pajamas." I located a parking spot by the public playground, quiet and still, not a soul in sight. Then there it came, that voice of reason, saying how ridiculous this was, did I really think people would be showing up in their pajamas for a public outdoor event? If I'd worn jeans, I would have likely been in the majority. The norm, after all, is to err on the conservative side, right? Steeling myself for the shame and embarrassment I was about to experience, I rounded the corner by the Page and Palette, hearing the laughter of party-goers, all wearing casual outdoor attire, I was sure. I stood in the shadows and studied the long, single-file line under the street lights, each presenting their ticket, each looking as if they had just tumbled out of bed: robes, sleep masks, plaid boxers, and nightshirts—not a pair of jeans in sight. I merged in front of a woman with pink sponge rollers and silky, floral, wrap robe and into the party. A drive-in movie was set up on the corner by the bookstore, gigantic screen mounted to the wrought-iron filigree columns. The Alabama/Auburn game was tied, fans in lawn chairs and old movie theater seats spilling popcorn as the extra point was missed. This was hard-core Alabama football territory, and I was thankful my purple-and-gold LSU nightshirt was back in Louisiana, or I would have had it on.

About midway down the block, the Stompknockers played "Sweet Home Alabama," as several hundred locals boogied in their nocturnal garb. I walked past them, close to the curb so as not to get caught up in a giant circle forming, dancers one by one moving to the center, performing their specialty steps.

The Waffle House was serving breakfast with an impressive setup in front of A Place Remembered; about twenty steel waffle makers cranked out their specialty, batter oozing from the sides of the contraptions, chefs in aprons scattering hash browns on griddles and on others, sausage. The evening breeze stirred the aroma into a tantalizing blend of warm vanilla and fried fare. An assembly-line team was pouring orange juice while their coworkers filled containers with warm syrup. Long, white-draped tables allowed party goers to be served then seated, or move down the block to pick up a glass of wine to sip with their evening breakfast. Further down De La Mere, a DJ, complete with colored strobe lights, took requests at the kids' disco party. The *Cupid Shuffle* blared with several dozen, from toddlers to teens, up and moving in sync.

Dodging a pair dressed in black turtlenecks, pants, and masks and carrying flashlights—cat burglars, of course—I stepped over a Chihuahua in a lime-green sleep mask, leash to match. I grabbed a plate and went to the back of the football game crowd, scoring a spot to sit next to a guy in orange jammies, shouting "War Eagle!" Glancing down at his blue-and-orange scuffies with the AU logo, I exhaled deeply, settling in as a spectator, finishing off my last bite of food. War Eagle man got up to put his plate in the trash, gestured toward my empty plate, took it, and said, "Save my seat?"

"Sure thing," I responded.

The tune "Land of a Thousand Dances" was moving the crowd to do the pony, the mashed potato, the jerk, everyone singing "naaaaa, na na na naaaaa." A pony-tailed woman wearing a nightshirt with a dog on the front signaled War Eagle man to join her. "My wife. After all this time, you'd think she'd remember I don't dance." Just then, the band broke into a lively Cotton-eyed Joe. Ponytail lady came flying through the crowd, grabbing War Eagle man with one hand and me with the other, pulling us both into the two-stepping swirl. "Where did ya come from, where did ya go, where did ya come from, Cotton-eyed Joe?" War Eagle man had wrangled loose and scrambled back to his chair while I was in the firm grip of the ponytail lady and the swarm of PJ-clad revelers. Suddenly, the circle stopped and faced inward and hand-clapping, slipper stomping began. Ponytail lady tightened her grip and tugged me to the center, where she let go and proceeded to perform a robust Irish step dance. Seeing no opening to exit, I, too, broke into the tap dancing, knee-lifting, straight-armed folk routine, the crowd shouting "Yeeeee haaaaah!"

The minute the music ended, I raced back to find my chair occupied. War Eagle man shrugged. "I see you've met my wife, Barbara Jean."

Ponytail lady chimed in with, "And I see you've met my Bud."

That's how it began; the friend I wasn't seeking appeared in a nightshirt that read *Be Yourself, Everyone Else is Already Taken.*

Over time, I learned that Barbara Jean's family was responsible for bringing Kudzu to the South, and that she kept a box of kitchen matches on the back of her toilet embellished with a sticker proclaiming *Redneck Air Freshener.* She knew the best places for finding eggs fresh from the farm and had a child-like sense of wonder at the ordinary. On one of our evening walks along Magnolia Beach, we heard the sound of drumbeats in the distance. "C'mon!" and she was headed down a narrow winding path into the trees, me following. The trail ended at a clearing behind the American Legion, on the beach. Flaming torches surrounded a circle of people playing various percussion instruments. "Join us!"" a woman with blond braids whispered as she moved to make a space. As I was gesturing "No thanks," Barbara Jean was positioning a set of bongos between her knees. A man to my left pulled a shaker from a bag on the ground, extending it to me. I studied the hard black objects connected with leather strips. "Goat's gonads," he whispered. "Shake them." Almost unconsciously, I was becoming a local, one of the contented, free spirits that filled this little town.

Eliot began to adapt to the fact that I would commute to and from the cottage, always eager to return home to my place on the bay. He would drive over occasionally, but never seemed to be drawn to the place. "Not all people are called to be here," I once heard someone comment.

Over time, I was seeing a new identity emerge: the woman I was—apart from the roles in Louisiana. The woman whose sense of wonder had expanded at the beauty all around her, whose heart was beginning to expand as I realized that people are mostly good and kind. I knew that I may never know or understand the what or why that brought me to this unconventional life, but I would likely forever be grateful for the path that brought me to that cottage by the bay.

CHAPTER TWENTY-SIX

I met Cherianne and Gary at the big pier, introduced by their dog, Roxie, a beagle/poodle mix. They both volunteered at The Haven, the local no-kill animal shelter, and on the weekends rescued sea turtles down at Gulf Shores. We would sit on the benches across from the rose garden, visiting with passersby, watching Roxie in the role of welcome committee chairdog.

"Gary and I have been invited to a dinner party Saturday night; would you like to join us?" Cherianne inquired. "We can pick you up."

Within a split-second, I assessed the proposal, wanting to ask a dozen questions. *So, what's the worst thing that can come of this, that I feel socially awkward for an evening?* Remembering my recent revelation that my sense of adventure seems to have disappeared, I agreed to go. "Yes, sounds fun!"

"Jeans will be fine, but bring a light jacket in case we sit outside on their deck, ok?" Cherianne instructed. "Fall evenings, you never know . . ." She pulled out her phone and asked my address, saying they'd be by around six. With that, Roxie was pulling her toward a great dane down on the beach. "See you then, Vicki!" And they were gone.

Second thoughts flooded in almost immediately. And questions like what was Cherianne's phone number in case I needed to cancel. Mostly that one. And what should I bring? I called Eliot.

"Geaux Tigers!" he answered. He was happiest during football season and his LSU team was playing Saturday night.

"Hey, Eliot, so I've been invited to this dinner party and I don't want to go and I should have said no and now I'm stressing and I don't know the people's last name who are picking me up and I can't call them and since I really would love to just put a note on the door that I had to go to the ER or something but I can't do that so what do you think I should bring?"

Fortunately, he totally understood, gleaning the essence and answering, "Wine."

"OK. What kind?"

"What will they be serving?" he asked.

"No clue," I responded.

"Well, don't they have a little wine store downtown?"

"As a matter of fact, they do. I'll go there in the morning. Eliot, I knew you would have the answer."

"Glad to help. Anything else?"

"Stay tuned. Hey, you want to come over and go with me?"

"Not on your life. First Saturday in November the Tigers play the Crimson Tide. You're on your own with this gig."

I left the wine store after answering, "No clue," to the *what will they be serving* question again, carrying the handled, slender signature red-and-white bag elegantly tied with raffia. I made a palette out of my sweatshirt in the bike basket, placing the bag on it.

Saturday evening, I sat on the swing, bag in hand, waiting. Eliot texted, "Ya got the goods?"

"Yes!" I responded.

"What kind did u get?"

"Don't know, skinny bottle, screw-on top, pretty bag."

"Uh oh."

"What?" I felt a panic creeping in. Just then, up drove Gary and Cherianne. I blinked, not moving, just staring at my mode of transportation, a red golf cart emblazoned with yellow flames streaking across the front.

"Well, c'mon, girl, hop on in!" Cherianne shouted.

I stood, dropping the cell phone. Stooping to retrieve it, I read Eliot's response: "Screw-on top???"

Four blocks from the cottage, the waterfront bay house was illuminated with carriage lanterns flickering light on the footpath, a canopy of white twinkle lights strung from the trees above. Laughter from inside encouraged Cherianne. "Pammie, we're heeeere!" A robust woman with blonde spikey hair emerged at the door, opening her arms and pulling me to her ample bosom, "You must be Vicki. Honey, come on in and make yourself at home." I handed her the wine, which she pulled out of the bag and remarked to the group that it would be perfect with dinner. I could have had anything in that bag and Pammie would have made me feel it was the perfect choice, no doubt.

Passing a sign in the foyer that read *Be Kind or Leave,* I was introduced to the group and Pammie's husband, Richard, a member of the clergy. Their house guest, a woman from North Carolina, appeared not to know anyone else, giving me a measure of comfort.

The long harvest table, made from Pammie's grandfather's barn door, held candles and pottery dinnerware on woven placemats. Long benches held five of us on each side, Pammie and Richard at each end. I faced the big glass windows looking out on the deck, seeing the leaves being blown about, assuming the water was just beyond. Fried green tomatoes followed by shrimp and grits left little room for dessert, an upside down warm gingerbread with praline glaze, poached pears baked inside, served with home made vanilla bean ice cream. The conversation and laughter had been easy and effortless, feeling much like a family gathering. Cherianne beamed in the candlelight. "I knew you'd enjoy this."

"You were right," I responded.

Note to self, I thought, *take more risks, Vicki.*

As I was exhaling my last shred of concern, feeling gratitude for the new connections, Pammie stood and said, "Ladies, I have the hot tub ready out on the deck. Sorry I don't have extra bathing suits, but I have a stack of fluffy bath sheets stacked on my bed. Fellas, y'all can go on downstairs and root for the Crimson Tide."

I froze as Cherianne and the other women were off to the bedroom. Except Miss North Carolina. At least that is what I was going to call her. Through the glass window, I watched Cherianne tiptoeing barefoot across the deck, wearing a blue-and-white striped towel. After her, Pammie and the two other women, giggling as they moved into the darkness, out of sight. I made eye contact with Miss North Carolina, who said, "I'm feeling a bit bloated so I think I'll stay inside."

BLOATED? Really? Is that the best you can come up with, honey? That's what I wanted to say. Or, better, *Meeeeeee too!* Instead, I swung my legs over the bench, waved at her, and said, "Awww, sorry to hear that."

Two towels remained on the bed. I stripped down and reached for the melon color one. In the process, I glimpsed my image in the full-length cheval mirror beside the dresser and paused, assessing my choices. Towel in one hand and reaching back for my jeans, I weighed the options, hearing shrieks of laughter in the distance outside. *Take more risks,* I reminded myself. I tossed the jeans and made a cantaloupe-colored sarong.

Cherianne had spotted me clenching my towel with both hands as I raced across to the hot tub glowing with underwater blue lighting. "Wooooooohoooooo, Vicki! Put your towel on one of those hooks over there on that fence, then climb up these stairs, and come on in!" *Hook over there? Stairs?* I surveyed the area, digesting the obstacle course necessary to prepare to enter the tub. I walked over to the fence, where four towels were hanging, yanked mine off and put it on the hook. Next, the stairs. Four wooden stairs leading up to the platform high above the small pool. I climbed up, serenaded by four women crooning, "There she is, Miss America." I was standing on the platform, looking down at four smiling faces, their buoyant bodies bobbing in the blue-lighted, bubbling swirl. Sitting down, I eased into the water below, feeling the thaw of melted inhibitions, glancing back toward the house, seeing Miss North Carolina still at the table alone.

VICKI ARMITAGE

And once the storm is over, you won't remember how you made it through, or how you managed to survive. You won't even be sure whether the storm is really over. But one thing is certain. When you come out of the storm, you won't be the same person who walked in. That's what the storm is all about.

Haruki Murakami

EPILOGUE

In my early days living in Fairhope, a city worker came and sat beside me on a bench at Magnolia Beach. The bench was inscribed with a beautiful tribute to a person who loved this stretch of sidewalk above the bay, moss draped oaks, and the sound of the waves gently lapping along the shore. He pulled a sandwich from a paper bag and unwrapped the waxed paper to reveal what looked to be ham, cheese, and iceberg lettuce on white bread. Like in a schoolboy's lunch, his wife had tucked a note inside. He chuckled as he shared his wife's thoughtfulness. The message held a scripture of encouragement, reminding him that all things work together for good. Between bites, he asked if I knew about the history of Mobile Bay and the original name on early maps. "It's the bay of the Holy Spirit," he shared. "Do your research or better yet, go down to the museum and the director will point you to the documents." He went on to say that some people speak of being drawn here.

As I sit here in my little cottage in the Fruit and Nut District, a few houses up from the beautiful bay, I have no doubt that I was drawn here. It didn't make sense to anyone, but the strong tug was undeniable.

We sold our home in Louisiana and Elliot retired and moved to Fairhope with me. Shortly thereafter, he passed away from a terminal illness.

Daily, I am thankful for the circumstances that brought me here to the sweet community and the pace, kind and welcoming at every turn.

It is my hope that someone who reads this book will find comfort in knowing that, no matter the circumstances, there is shelter from the storm and steering currents that will lead you there.

STEERING CURRENTS

ABOUT THE AUTHOR

Vicki Armitage was the owner of Vicki's Dance Centers and saw thousands of aspiring dancers come through her doors, many who moved on to become dancers on Broadway, in film, at theme parks, and in dance ministries throughout the world. Many won national and international titles.

She was a featured guest on the *Oprah Winfrey Show* and attended Harvard Business School.

As a writer, Vicki was selected through juried admission four times to participate in Aspen Words, a prestigious literary festival. She was also published in *Chicken Soup for the Soul.*

Vicki enjoyed her time as a member of the Fairhope Writer's Group and has published stories in their anthologies and guides.

Her community of Fairhope, Alabama, is rich with creatives, always providing an encounter that leaves her grateful for the journey that brought her there. Her children, Kelly and Robby, along with her grandchildren, Ashlee, Madeline, Jillian and Jack are sources of joy as they pursue their unconventional lives.

vicki@vickiarmitage.com

Made in the USA
Coppell, TX
06 July 2024

34258054R00132